HE WROTE HER EVERY DAY

Gail Lindenberg

SAPERE
BOOKS

HE WROTE HER EVERY DAY

Published by Sapere Books.

11 Bank Chambers, Hornsey, London, N8 7NN,
United Kingdom

saperebooks.com

ISBN: 978-1-912786-45-9

Preface

7.18.44
Ft. MacArthur, Calif.

Dear Butch:

How is my honey tonight? Here's hoping that you are still eating those three squares a day. The food here is O.K. but I'd much rather I was with you right now eating a good steak or something.

Am feeling a bit woozy from the shots today, but so is the whole bunch. Doc says it wears off in a few hrs. We are all through with processing except for getting our dog tags...

There are people here from all over these United States and every one of them has a story to tell. They all have an idea about where we go from here and how things are going to be, but I try not to listen to the rumors too much. In a place like this, you can hear anything at all, and you usually do. That doesn't mean that any of it is true, though.

Hugh Wilhite is supposed to be here tonight. I sure hope I run into him to give him "Ye Olde Raspberry." One consolation is that everybody here is not sent to the same place, not at the same time. I talked to one fellow here who had been loafing around this place for 2 months. Don't like the loafing, but would still like to see you once in a while.

Hope you got the picture ok.

All my love,

Jim

"Where on earth did 'Butch' come from?" Reading and scanning one of the letters my mother had given me to preserve for safe-keeping, I glanced once more at the thin and fragile envelopes lined up in the brown box as though in regimented files, waiting further inspection. The ribbons that bind the envelopes are pale and tired, sweet ties whose job is done. Each folded letter, (written in pencil until the first care package arrived to provide my father with a pen) opens to tell part of a tale from time gone by. In 1944, my mother, Irene Hendrickson was just a girl at twenty, young and fresh from Platner, Colorado, where the population was only slightly more than her age. She watched her husband of two years, James William Hendrickson, Jr., known to her as Jim, go off to Camp Roberts in California to train to fight as a soldier in World War II. He could have stayed home as the third of two brothers already working for the war effort, but he wanted to rescue his brother, Bill, from a German prison camp. His letters began arriving regularly, and she saved each one with care. He had promised to write daily and the letters, V-mails, postcards and journals we have are a promise he seems to have kept.

My mother began to murmur softly, answering my earlier question and gently interrupting my thoughts. "Butch? Yes, he did call me that. I'd almost forgotten. That first letter was written, what ... seventy years ago? You know, Gail, I always thought that your dad was a bit surprised at how tough I was." Irene doesn't look tough. She is, at eighty-nine years old, just one hundred pounds, frail and fragile in appearance. Spend just a bit of time with her though, and you soon recognize her dogged strength, rather like that last leaf left on the tree after a wind storm. "Your dad worried about leaving me to go to war, but he looked at me and said, 'You know, Butch, you are going to be just fine while I am gone.' And he was right, too. Your dad calling me Butch never felt like an insult," she says with a smile. "Butch is a tough-guy name and you know I had to be tough, there was just no other choice. I was alone here in

Yuma, Arizona, a town I'd never even visited before we drove down here to get married."

In 1942, at the tender age of eighteen, Irene left home and followed her brother, Chuck to Burbank, California. When I ask her about this time, she chortles at the memory.

"Chuck had a job in one of the aircraft factories and that kept him from active service for a while. That's where he and your father met. Chuck and I roomed with a bunch of kids about our age in a boarding house. We even shared beds by working different shifts. To wash the sheets, one of us would have to sleep our turn on the couch until the linens dried on a clothes line out back. I still like the scent of sun-dried bed linens.

"When I crawled into that bed after work, I would find it still warm from the one who slept there before me. I never thought a thing about it. I would just collapse with my own blanket wrapped around me and sleep like the dead until the next one got off shift and woke me up. We never needed any alarm clock, that's for certain.

"Your dad lived in our boarding house — lots of people had turned large homes into rentals like that. Jim and Chuck got to know each other first. They got along like brothers before I even met Jim. He was so handsome and charming. I remember he used to say that in his next life he planned to be rich instead of handsome. And then he would laugh like he didn't mean it. But he *was* handsome, more so than he knew. And such a gentleman, too.

"We were both so green, really. But your dad had a way about him that made him seem much more than just a kid from the sticks. Other folks always looked to him for direction. I guess you would call it *presence*. Whatever it was, I knew I was lucky to catch his eye."

"Why didn't Dad join up sooner? The war had been going on two years before he went to Camp Roberts."

"Your father did have a health history that caused problems the first time he tried to enlist. In his first Army physical right out of high school, the Army doctor saw his scar. He had emergency surgery at about age twelve. Folks back then didn't go to the doctor right away. Most tried to use home remedies. He was on his way home from school, and he got a bad pain in his side. He just tried to tough it out. The pain got worse, and about a week later, his appendix burst. Even then they didn't take him to the doctor until much later when they couldn't bring down his fever.

"Doctor Powell operated as soon as he could get him to the hospital, but the poison had already spread. He had to sit at home to heal for an entire school year, his leg swollen from the spread of infection. That whole year, after the operation, he did schoolwork at home. Good thing he liked to read. The teachers tested him when he returned, and he had out-paced his class. They put him ahead a grade. So he gained two school years by staying home for one. He also gained a ton of weight from sitting and eating his mother's cooking. He didn't keep the weight on, though. The family lived up by the Imperial Dam then. And so he swam across the Colorado River and back every day until he reduced to his usual spare build.

"He came out of it stronger than ever and graduated a year ahead of his own class; but he always had a slight shortness to one side of his body. The Army doctor said he thought it looked like Jim had been in a knife fight rather than through a surgical procedure."

"So he didn't get into the Army the first time because of the scar?"

"That's right. That's part of it anyway. Jim said it bothered the Army doctor who gave him his physical. He told him he wouldn't be fit to fight. Your father felt shamed. He knew he was physically fit. So he kept trying. He stayed working for Lockheed, but reapplied as often as he could. They would have taken him the second time, but he was turned down again and again because of his work. Lockheed placed a hold on his acceptance.

"He argued with them about that. Your dad was a skilled welder, and the factories kept as many of those men working as they could until they finally started letting women take some of the jobs. Now my job — I was just a rivet bucker. The men on my shift had all been called to fight with no fuss from Lockheed. There were plenty of women to do that work. You've heard of Rosie the Riveter?"

Of course I had. The year before, my sister sent my mother the famous poster with her face photoshopped over the original model in the picture. At age twenty, Irene looked enough like the original Rosie to have posed for it herself. The poster features the image of Rosie the Riveter making a fist to show her muscle. The words "We Can Do It!" float in a word bubble coming from her mouth. Rosie the Riveter became a popular icon created to inspire American women to enter the work force. During the war, twenty million women took jobs, most of them for the first time.

I point to the wall where the mock poster hangs. My mother gives the framed picture pride of place on her kitchen wall. The Arizona sun beams kindly on the face of Irene as Rosie who stares from the frame with determined pride.

"They had plenty of Rosie gals to do the work, and the country encouraged women to join the effort. There just weren't enough of the young men left! But your dad kept going back and forth to the Army recruiters and to the supervisor at Lockheed. He wanted to fight in that war and help end it. He had decided it was his job to go after your Uncle Bill.

"I can remember the day he got his notice of service, and he came home so happy I just had to be glad for him. Neither one of us knew where it would lead. All of our plans would have to change. If he'd stayed at Lockheed, we would probably have made our home in California. And he wouldn't have had to walk across Europe in the snow either.

"But I made him promise me that he would write me every single day he was gone. And one thing about your dad, if he said he would do something — it got done."

My father fought hard with officials at Lockheed and the recruitment center, determined to get into the fighting. By 1944, the Army was ready to take any man who was vertical, and so, once he convinced Lockheed that they could survive without his welding skills, he joined up with enthusiasm, in spite of the fact that he knew he would be leaving his young wife behind.

"He was stationed at Camp Roberts for a good while. And he finally got some weekend passes home," my mother tells me.

"I sure wish we had your letters to him," I remark. "It's difficult to fill in the blanks and I've noticed that there are gaps in the dates between his letters. I thought you told me he wrote daily."

"Naturally, he didn't write me when he was home on a pass. And I didn't receive all the letters he wrote either. He had other people to write to as well. Some of those precious letters did not get shared with me. I have to say the Army was good about delivering letters — eventually. But there would be weeks without a word, usually when he was moving from one place to the next. But still, some of the letters never made it to me at all.

"And as for my letters to him, he certainly had no way to keep them. Can you see him toting all those silly things all over Germany? Why, he wasn't even allowed to keep much more than a photo in his wallet."

"So," I resume the conversation, "Dad was trained at Camp Roberts? Where is that?"

"Camp Roberts lies about three hours north of Burbank where I lived, but I got to see him pretty often in those early days. Jim would earn a weekend pass and usually be able to hitch a ride with a soldier who had a car. I got to meet a few of those boys, but they always hurried off to their own sweethearts. Since I was sharing the house with other girls, your dad and I would try to find a place to go and be a couple, you know… Sometimes we headed to a cabin a family owned up in Lake Arrowhead, east of San Bernardino. We would drive with Chuck and his new wife, Carolyn. Larry, their oldest, was just a baby. We had good times those weekends.

"But when we didn't have time or money to take the trips, my roommates were real good to let us have the house to ourselves when they could. We made our times fun in spite of the war worries. Everyone helped each other over the rough spots."

Jim's letters reveal a very careful portion of their experience in those years, one I am hoping to find out more about. Mom's face glows, lighting up with quiet joy as she recalls those bygone times. My mother's gift to me of the letters is becoming a puzzle I am eager to solve. I just wish my father could be here to remember with us. It is his story. But it is also our nation's story, one with a lasting impact on world events that resonate still. More than ever, I am yearning to hear my father's voice through his letters.

I: Training Camp

Chapter One

7.20.44
Ft. MacArthur, Calif.

Hello Butch,

Have finally got off detail and have the rest of the night off. When I phoned you today I was really burned up about everything in general. As I told you, I was on K.P. from 8 yesterday until 8 A.M. and right after that they put me on detail fitting clothes on the boys—why, I don't know, because I can't tell one size from another.

Am all dressed up in O.D.s now and just went over and got more pictures taken, which are enclosed. One isn't too hot, but we don't have much to do at night around here and the pictures are only 3 for 25 cents.

Eddie Cantor is supposed to be here tonight, so I think I'll go on over and take a gander at the old duck. I've been looking out for Hugh Wilhite to show up, but so far I've seen neither hide nor hair of him.

There is a guy on the old piano that's been playing the same piece of boogie-woogie over and over for the last two hours. Nobody has shot him yet. The guys are still yelling for more.

One thing, a place like this does make you realize just how much simple things, like washing dishes together, kidding you about being fat, etc. etc, mean. I didn't think confinement of this type would be so hard to take. Don't mind the work, the waiting and being shoved around, if I could just see you once in a while.

Tell Charlie Clarence and Daisy hello for me and keep your fingers crossed so I can see you this Sat. Will probably know by noon and phone you.

Loads of love,
James

Jim carefully folded the letter around the photograph, putting the best one on top. He thought it was a good picture, and he smiled when he thought of Irene opening the envelope and seeing him in his uniform. The olive drab color of the O.D.s looked brown in the sepia-toned photo. His sandy blonde hair was short (the Army's choice of course), and he thought Irene would like his smile. He figured she would carry it with her and show it around to all the people he knew.

As promised, Jim would write some little bit of news to Irene every day as a way to keep her close. He might not get a whole letter written at once, he could already see that the Army didn't consider giving soldiers time to think, let alone time to write down their thoughts. But writing gave him a connection to his wife and the people he cared about back home.

He hated leaving Irene alone, so far away from her family. He could picture her, still toiling away on the airplane wings in the Lockheed plant. His brother, Bill, might have flown one of those planes she was helping to put together. He shook his head remembering how Bill couldn't wait to leave college and join up after Pearl Harbor. Always their mother's favorite son, he wanted to fly, and the Army was glad to give him the opportunity. To add to their mother's despair, Bill had been shot down over Germany in his very first action, and remained there, a prisoner of war in an undisclosed location.

Jim could have sat out the war at home with his wife, but he had a mission. He had set about to enlist so as to get the war ended and bring his brother home. And now here he sat, in Camp Roberts, California, dressed in Army gear on a cot in the barracks.

Jim needed something else to keep his mind occupied until he could give his weary body some rest. He would rather hit the hay, but with all the commotion of so many soldiers milling about, there was no chance of getting any sleep until lights out. He spotted a fellow he recognized from his unit just as the guy hollered at him.

"Hey, Jim, you scalped anybody yet?"

The soldier's name came to him and Jim laughed. "If I did, Keller, you'd have been the first in line!" Jim had told a story about the Yuma Indians the other night, and it had sure made a hit with the guys. Of the fellows at "good old Ft. MacArthur," most were farm boys from the Midwest who held odd notions of *Injuns*. That came from reading dime novels and stories of the wildness that exaggerated the savagery of the Old West.

When Jim told them that his great granddad had been a Cherokee chief, they grew unusually quiet for a while, eyeballing him with wary glances, averting gazes when he looked their way. Jim knew he didn't look Cherokee with his blue eyes and dark blond hair. He didn't mind letting them chew on his information a bit so they could adjust their thinking about Wild West savages.

"You heading down to see Cantor?" Keller asked. A farmer's son, Keller hailed from Ohio. Tall and blonde, he looked farm-fed with strong teeth and eyes that stayed wide all the time. Jim imagined he would look that way himself except for the fact that he was tired enough to sleep standing.

"Yep, I figured I would get an eye-full of him if I could. You headed over to the show too, Private?"

"Yessir, *Injun* Jim," the young man replied. "I aim to see a big name any time the show is paid for by the Army. Free is a good price to pay."

Jim smiled and answered, "I bet you aren't the only one who feels that way. But it's not really free, is it? Seems like it's the least the Army can do for us, considering…"

As they walked towards the center of the compound, Jim was thinking that Fort MacArthur was a lucky draw for him. The induction center sat poised over the San Pedro Bay, established in the late 1800's as a line of defense for the port of Los Angeles. The officer in charge of their orientation lecture spent a great deal of time explaining how lucky they were to find themselves billeted where The Great Los Angeles Air Raid had taken place on February 19, 1942. Ft. McArthur stood as the last outpost against foreign attack, perched on the Pacific and proud with shiny, brand new guns, not yet tested by war action. Part of their orientation included a retelling of the most memorable night yet at the military installation known as Angel's Gate. *Daily News* reporter Matt Weinstock had published a report after talking to a man who had served in one of those Army batteries and the new soldiers were given a pamphlet recounting his story:

Early in the war things were pretty scary and the Army was setting up coastal defenses. At one of the new radar stations near Santa Monica, the crew tried in vain to arrange for some planes to fly by so that they could test the system. As no one could spare the planes at the time, they hit upon a novel way to test the radar. One of the guys bought a bag of nickel balloons and then filled them with hydrogen, attached metal wires, and let them go. Catching the offshore breeze, the balloons had the desired effect of showing up on the screens, proving the equipment was working. But after traveling a good distance offshore and to the south, the nightly onshore breeze started to push the balloons back towards the coastal cities. The coastal radar picked up the metal wires and the searchlights swung automatically on the targets, looking on the screens as aircraft heading for the city. The ACK-ACK started firing and the rest was history.

Most of the other guys who arrived at the camp on the same day as Jim had traveled long distances to get here. Not him — he had just zoomed north a few hours from Burbank where he and Irene had lived as newlyweds just over a year before. Close enough to visit his wife on weekends, Jim hoped he could finagle a pass and find a ride back over the Hollywood Hills to visit her. Of the complaints heard in the barracks about the food or the hard bunkbeds, guys griped most about being so far from home.

"What kept you away from the first part of this fight, Keller?"

"Well, Jim, I couldn't leave my pa working the land by himself. I waited for my kid brother to get big enough to do the heavy lifting. Just the thought of my mom leaving her kitchen to run the tractor — farming is hard work, you know?"

How well Jim knew. He would be home if it weren't for Bill landing in that German prison camp. He also knew that there wasn't anything he wanted more in life than to be a farmer once the war ended. His father owned land back home. With a Texaco station to manage, rental homes to landlord, and desert land ready to homestead or improve with crops, Jim hoped to take charge of a parcel of land and farm it. He'd worked in the station as long as he could remember, pumping gas and shooting the breeze with all the old cronies who used his father's station as their own town hall. Some of his holdings already planted in citrus showed promise of golden wealth. The war had put all of those plans on the back burner.

"I understand what you're saying, Ohio," Jim said. "It's not easy to turn your back on family and put your life on hold. But like you, I felt like there was a call to answer and I wanted to do my own part to drive Hitler back into whatever cave he crawled out of. Now, let's get on over to that theater hall before all the good seats get taken up by those guys from Kentucky. I want to have something to talk about in tonight's letter to Irene."

Keller grinned at that and began to walk with a forced-march pace. "Yeah, we noticed. It's like you aren't even with us when you put that pen to paper every night. But your name is hollered every mail call. Nothing's come for me yet. Didn't reckon I'd miss it, and I know my folks aren't much for writing. It must be nice to know someone is thinking about you."

"Yes," Jim murmured to himself, "nice it is." But he was beginning to see mail as a poor substitute for being home. As they headed into the hall, bright lights across the doorway blinked at them, an attempt to give the impression of a fancy Hollywood nightclub. Jim ducked his head under the flashy glare and started to take notes in his head for what he would say to Irene in the next letter. He sure wished she was here with him to see the show.

Chapter Two

25.7.44
Camp Roberts, Calif.

Hello Butch:

Got in here last night and this is the first time I've had a chance to send a letter. We are to be reassigned again, so unless it's an emergency, don't write till I let you know—if you do write put down:

Pvt. James William Hendrickson—39593513

Camp Roberts, California

From what the older guys here have been saying, this is a rough deal here. I'm beginning to believe them. It was a beautiful ride up till about 20 miles from here and then it got into rough country. They took us over to the PX last night and I drank my first and last bottle of beer here— "Whew!"

Some of us will stay here 17 weeks and they will ship some of us out. If I can make transportation connections, I might be able to see you a couple of times while here. I've got my fingers crossed.

The food is O.K. here but nothing to brag about and all you have to sleep in is 1 bed mattress, 2 blankets and 1 pillow—no sheets, mattress covers or pillow cases. It gets kinda scratchy before morning.

Well honey, I hope this finds you well and I'll write whenever I get the chance.

Love,

Jim

P.S. If I live through this, I sure ought to be a helluva tough hombre.

Jim hated to ask Irene not to write, but he didn't want her letters to go missing while he waited for the Army to make a definite assignment for his quarters. Since he could already see that his time was no longer his own to command, Jim put his thoughts on paper at every free moment, even if that meant sneaking into the latrine when the others were bedded down for the night. The short letter he had managed to mail earlier took three days to compose.

He and the other recruits from Ft. MacArthur bussed in the night before weren't yet assigned to a platoon or a barracks. A gut-fear clenched his stomach that the Army might lose him in all the crowds of men shuffling here and there. Jim had never seen so many people all at once. He had been in the Army just ten days, had already been moved three times, and had bedded down with a different set of strangers each time. He craved news from back home and wanted to hear Irene's voice.

A hall that opened after morning chow boasted a bank of shiny phones. The long lines promised a long wait, but here he stood, on feet already sore from last night's "walk" around the compound, watching the soldier at the head of his line hold a receiver, and wishing the guy would hurry up and finish his call. Eye-balling the frozen line, he nudged the soldier in front of him.

"Has it moved since you got here?"

"Not as I reckon," the soldier replied. Jim thought this man looked a bit older than most of the others he'd met up with so far. With hints of grey beginning above his ears, he spoke with a Midwesterner's drawl to his speech.

"I think there's near 'bout 100,000 of us in this camp … and most of them stand right in that line up yonder. Did you land here with the new wave from LA yesterday night?"

Jim replied, "Sure did. Have you been here a while, sir?"

"Ha! Don't *sir* me yet. Name's Brewster, from Iowa. I don't aim to require a man to salute me any time soon."

Passing the time with some conversation seemed like a good notion, since they were doomed to share the space waiting for the phone. Some of the fellows stood silent, perhaps practicing what they might say once their turn finally came. After all, a phone fee cost according to how long the conversation lasted. Being long-winded or unprepared for conversation could be expensive. Some of the older men exhibited a thousand-yard stare of resigned frustration. Jim was glad Brewster was a talker.

"I've been here two weeks. It feels like a lot longer than that, I'll tell you. What's your name, soldier?"

"I'm James," Jim answered and put out his hand for a shake. "What kind of ride have you had here? At Ft. MacArthur we were told to plan to bunk here at least seventeen weeks."

"I wouldn't set my watch by what they tell you. Seems like things change pretty quick, even though the time passes slow. Y'all joined our all-nighter right out of the bus last night, I saw. Seems like this man's Army wants to make sure we can all walk, wherever they expect to send us. Between marches and the calisthenics, I have a hard time stayin' awake during the lectures. And they surely do have a few of those to sit through, I can vow."

Jim spoke up hopefully. "Chow's pretty good though. Breakfast this morning was just fine. Course I was so hungry I would probably have enjoyed chewing on this big old boot I'm wearing."

Brewster laughed out loud. "I have yet to talk to a man who was issued the right size shoes. It's a wonder we can walk at all in boots that belong on some other guy's feet size. Why do you reckon we can't get clothes to fit?"

Jim smiled back ruefully. "My first job as a military man was to issue the clothes to the other boys in my outfit. I had no idea what I was doing, so I just threw something at them that looked about right. Now I've got to wonder how many fellows march around cussing me because they have on duds that don't fit. I guess once we get our guns, I'd better watch my own back. Some unhappy guy with sore feet might just shoot me because his boots are too tight."

They shared a laugh as the line edged up a bit, and Jim's mood lightened in the company of this stranger. Most of the men he had talked to seemed to be good sorts.

"Hey, Brewster, looks like you're up soon to grab that phone. Make it quick, will you? I have a wife to talk to just as soon as you get done flapping your jaw!"

Brewster gave a grin and raced to catch the phone before the receiver settled on the hook. Jim watched him talking, staying back to allow some privacy. Finally, Brewster waved him over to grab the phone and Jim dialed, imagining Irene running to grab the ringing phone in their small house back in Burbank. He glanced at the still-waiting soldiers as the phone rang and rang unanswered. With each continued ring, his spirits drooped. His guts sagged all the way into his own too-big boots, but he forced himself to put the phone back on the hook.

Dragging himself away from the still-long lines of men, he hoped they had better luck. He wished he could have let Irene know when to expect calls. Then he realized — what was he thinking? Irene worked this time of day! The realization made him feel even more disconnected from his young wife. Their world as newlyweds in Burbank had brought closeness, and they had shared their thoughts to the point of being able to finish each others' sentences. He could feel that world fracturing into two separate, and lonely, planets.

He could have used his nickel to phone his mother. She would be home and fuming not to have heard from him. But his first yearning had been to hear Irene's voice.

Jim found a place under the shade of a tree outside the hall in a small park-like area. Others like him, who evidently didn't have a place to call home yet, had stowed their gear in an enclosure just inside the compound. They had been corralled right off the bus and herded out to spend the night marching. Close order drills required them to carry their field packs.

Now, under the shade of the tree near the phone center, he decided he might try to catch a nap before the noon meal. Beds would be assigned after, but they probably wouldn't get to sleep until nightfall — if then. He used his pack as a pillow and settled back to gaze at the sky, in hopes that sleep would come to heal his sore feet and soothe his spirits.

Other married soldiers at Ft. MacArthur had talked about moving their wives up close to Camp Roberts. But the town of Paso Robles, as well as a lot of other little towns surrounding the camp, were a hell of a mess, all overcrowded with war brides and families. His "Butch" would have no one up here she knew, and tough as she was, she would be better off with the friends they had made in Burbank. She still had her job there too.

He still felt annoyed that he had wasted all that time, standing in line to make a call that would go unanswered. He could have used the time to write, or to study for the next Officer Candidate test. That was another one of things he had hoped to share with Irene, that he had passed his first test with top scores. Maybe Brewster from Ohio wasn't looking to have anyone salute him, but Jim wouldn't mind moving up the line if he could. It would mean more in the pay packet, too. From what he had seen of the officers in his two weeks with the Army, the folks giving orders were just like anybody else.

Chapter Three

8-6-44
4:30 P.M.

Hello Sweetie:

...I have not missed one day of writing to you since July 14th and some days I have written two. I always try to write quite plainly—at least on the envelope. I didn't get a letter from you today, though I did get one yesterday.

One of the fellow's wives came up to camp yesterday from San Francisco. She waited around all day and only got to see him for about two minutes as we were moving. He sure was a sick guy, and I guess she was awfully disappointed.

They tried to charge me for eight minutes on that last phone call to you. I finally argued them into letting me off for three minutes. The old bags in the phone center can't count!

8:30 P.M.

Just got back from a little exercise with the soldiers. Not much is scheduled in advance around here except chow, and we can't always count on that either. I am getting used to this place now. I expect to move once a week for the duration. I just get my clothes hung up on those hangers you sent me and somebody yells— "Fall out in two minutes with all your gear."

Honey, I will always try to call you at noon on Sundays, but today I didn't finish until 11:45 and it took me until 2:20 to get the call through.

Do you know that in eight days we will have been married a whole year and five months? I want you to know that I have been happier in that time than any other time in my life and I hope we can make that year and five months grow into a hundred years and five months.

It seems like years since I've seen you—and long years at that. I still have your pictures, although I want another or two when I get down there. (Where ever there will be.)

If I get a pass, I think I have a ride to L.A. with a Sergeant here, but of course it depends on whether we both get passes on the same week end.

Honey, I may not get to write to Charlie or Chuck till Sunday, so tell them I'll write everybody Sunday—unless I'm with you.

All my love,

Jim

I've got this many kisses coming to me. xxxxxxxxxxxxxxxxxxxxxx

"Hey, Hendrickson! You still writing to your wife? Get on over here and take a hand of cards. We need some fresh blood in this game." Jim looked up from his writing and shook his head at a small group of soldiers gathered around their cots. He had not paid any attention to them, he was so immersed in his writing.

The entire camp was restricted to barracks and no one knew why. Glad for the break from drills and lectures, Jim thought to himself that the Army would either make a better man of him or kill him. For now, he knew he was doing as well or better than most of the other fellows.

A fairly harmless pastime while waiting for orders, the card games kept their minds off troubles. But Jim wanted to get a whole letter written while he had some precious down time. While he wrote, he didn't even hear the commotion of the eleven other men in the quarters. He was surprised when he looked up to see them staring at him.

"I'm in, soldiers, keep your shirts on." Jim grinned ruefully as he grudgingly left his bunk, tucking Irene's letter in his kit bag and grabbing some change and a few dollars to buy into the game. Before he could sit down at one of the make-shift poker tables made from cots, Keller from Ohio came bursting through the door full of news, and everyone turned in his direction, ready to abandon penny-ante poker for a chance at some real excitement.

"Guess what, fellas," Keller hollered, "the whole damn camp is restricted. They've called the M.P.s out from surrounding towns and there are no passes or furloughs granted until further notice — from officers on down."

Jim groaned with most of the other men to hear the news. He had hoped to get that weekend with Irene.

"Did you find out what's happening, Keller? This isn't an air raid warning, is it?"

That was a sobering thought. Three weeks in this man's Army did not inspire much confidence that these green boys would know what to do if the enemy brought the battle to American shores. There had been quite a bit of talk since the Germans had started to bomb England and most folks thought that the Japs might turn their sights on the coast. Training had barely begun, and some of the farm boys hadn't mastered how to salute a lieutenant properly, let alone follow his orders with any skill.

"No one is sharing anything out loud that I could find. The brass hats keep disappearing behind closed doors while the NCOs run around looking for someone to yell at. I had to keep my head down and look like I was busy. I was slinging hash in the officer's mess when the orders sounded, and I stayed to finish K.P." Keller looked around with a wry smile on his face. "I don't volunteer for chores, but I thought I could keep my ears open and maybe get the skinny. No dice. Nobody's saying word one."

Jim groaned in concert with the other grim-faced young men gathered around Keller, all of them drooping with disappointment or disgust. He wasn't the only one who had been looking forward to a weekend away from camp.

Jim spoke up in the heavy silence, "There's no use listening to rumors anyway. Deal out a hand of poker, fellas, and I'll let all of you contribute to Jim's Buy-a-ticket-home fund. Ante up, men, before somebody comes in to give us more bad news."

The guys regrouped and jostled to make room for Keller. They played poker into the night, as they would for many other nights to follow, as another day of service drew to a close. The card game blocked out any chance to think deeply about what dangers might lie ahead and, for a while, the soldiers forced laughter until the optimism of human nature fostered an ephemeral, but genuine happiness in the company of strangers upon whom their lives might ultimately depend.

Chapter Four

8/21/44
8:30 P.M.
Monday

Dearest Irene:
Got back to camp O.K. and on time too. We had to stop quite a bit because a couple of the guys were a bit under the weather.

Received three letters from my honey today and one from Mom with a picture of Dad and $5.00 in it. Darn her anyway, she is too good to everybody. There was also a card from Bill. He couldn't say much, but it is good to know he is not having too tough a time.

Also got a package from Virginia with some candy and nuts. Sure are good. Will have to get my little self busy and write everybody a letter, but you still come first anytime, anywhere and you had better not forget it.

I sure did have a swell time over the weekend. Wish that would happen to yours truly every day. I feel a lot better and my morale has come up about 1000%. You give me a lift without a letdown. (Believe I got that off of a cigarette advertisement, but it is still the truth.)

Dammit honey, I've got to cut this short as the lights are going out and they are having bed check tonight. Will make up this short letter as soon as possible.

All my love,
James
Those socks fit perfect honey, thanks again.

Sept. 10, 1944
Camp Roberts, Calif.

Dearest Irene:

After I phoned you yesterday, I called Mom. She says if I am needed to straighten things out there in Yuma, she will go to the Red Cross and try to get me a leave. Pop's leg is pretty bad. Both bones right below the knee were broken and they had to operate. As old as he is, it will be about a year, I think, before he can walk.

It was one of the kids that hang around the station who ran over him and dragged him 12 feet before they got the car stopped. Sure do wish I could go down and straighten things out.

So Chuck didn't make it home. That is what's known around here as a Tough Situation and believe me, there are a lot of them.

I sent the card I got from Bill to Mom and Pop. It might cheer them up a bit. Sure hope Pop doesn't take it too hard. He has worked hard all his life and the monotony will sure get him.

Am gaining back the weight I lost so you had better get busy and get yours back too.

I think it's a sure thing that James will get down to 2117 A Scott Road this weekend. Will go over now and clean up my mess kit. Wish we were washing dishes together now instead.

All my love,

Jim

(Hell of a place for a pen to run dry, isn't it? How about a date next Sat. nite? We might be able to have some fun.)

9/12/44 Camp Roberts, Calif.
12:35 Noon

Dearest Irene:

Am in the old barracks at lunchtime again. We have been running the bayonet assault course this morning. Sure is lots of fun batting the targets around with a bayonet.

9:30 P.M.

Hello again, Sugar.

At noon they called us out in a hurry to go to a class on Scouting. A Scout seems to get a rough deal in the Army. He goes about 500 yds. in front of the main force of men and his main purpose is to draw the enemy's fire. A Scout's life is evidently a short one when you are in actual combat.

Tonight I was roped in on a cleanup detail for a camp show. Got a front seat, though, for the work I did. Do you remember the Irish tenor, Jimmy O'Brien of the "Blackouts"? He has been inducted and is here at Camp Roberts. Looks like they eventually get them all, doesn't it? They also had one of Spike Jones' guitar players and, of course, they had Sonny Heideman, the guy who used to play trumpet for Horace Height.

Mom H wrote that she may have to get me a leave. Hate to interrupt my training, but the folks' welfare comes before my so-called "Army Career." If I should have to go down we'll see each other for a while anyway. You'll have to come to Yuma.

Seems like K.P. will hit me Thursday, so will probably see you this Sat. nite. Sure do hope so anyway. Looks like James will be about broke when he gets there.

The company is having a party tomorrow nite at the mess hall to celebrate our scores on the rifle range. All in all, the company did very good on the shooting.

Think I'll sign up for the Officer's Candidate School this week. Not much chance of making it any more, but there's no harm in trying. And I have passed all the tests to get there.

Lights are out and I'm in the latrine finishing this. I had better close before some son-of-a-gun catches me at it. Goodnight Sweetheart. Still think of you 48 hours a day.

XXXXXXXX from Jim in the latrine.

September 19, 1944
Camp Roberts, California

Hi Sweetie,

Glad you made it back to the apartment all right. Had a pretty good day today. We are still getting up too damned early and staying up too late, but outside of that we are enjoying it more.

When I say that, don't get the idea that I like the life though, it's just that I am getting used to it. The only life I will ever like is with a little gal by the name of Bernice Irene Ison Hendrickson and don't you forget it.

I think I can stand this place for the duration, but after that, nuts!! Could have signed up for Officer's training but they keep you for 3 years regardless of when the war ends—so to hell with it. From the way it looks here, a yard bird is the best thing to be in the Army.

Got a card from Ruth tonight. Have to get busy and answer some letters pretty soon. You are the only one I ever seem to find time to write to and then the time is pretty slim.

Had a fire drill tonight. They demonstrated the different types of fire extinguishers to us and gave out the glad news that some night soon they are going to get us out of bed in the middle of the night for another fire drill. You should have heard the groan that went up.

Had some tracer bullet firing today and some machine gun instruction. Can't figure out why they make us put guns together blindfolded all the time. We don't hardly know what they look like in the daylight. Enough baloney for tonight, sweetheart.

Give my love to Mrs. J.W., Jr. and goodnight.

Jim

P.S. In your letter you sounded as if you thought I didn't have a good time last week end. Honey, whenever you are around, I have fun.

Jim finished the second glass of draft beer and decided he had enough brew in him to make it look like he was happy to celebrate. He had to shake his head about getting an invitation to a beer bust from the Army to celebrate his shooting skills. Especially since showing up was mandatory.

He looked around the hall at all the men. Over a hundred of them circled the large room like a herd of drought-parched animals afraid that the well would run dry before they got their share of the wet stuff. Full kegs lined up in shining rows like palm trees at a desert oasis, a sparkling promise of an abundant flow for all.

"Hey there, Hendrickson!" The sergeant had a mug in his hand and a smile on his face, something Jim didn't often see from any of the higher-ups. "I saw you last week sitting right up front at the show the Canadians put on for us."

"Yeah, that was me, all right. I pulled the set-up detail and the front seat was my consolation prize. It was a good show. We got all worked up for the machine gun party afterwards."

Jim wasn't shy with the sergeant. Even though the man had to be older than he was, probably pushing thirty, Jim thought he was a square-shooter, a good leader who treated them well. Jim had never crossed any wires with him — and didn't intend to either. He was the kind of man Jim could admire.

"I heard you pulled the plug on Officer's Candidate School. Why did you do that?"

"I don't want to make a career of the Army after all. When this war is over, I want to try to get my life back to where it was before all the shooting started."

"I think most of us feel that way, Jim. I know I do. I don't have a wife or kids back home, but I still would like to get back to that farm land where I was raised and help my folks with the planting. They work too hard, and there aren't enough of us boys around to pick up the slack. But I had spotted you for officer material, and I'm not the only one."

Jim nodded his head once, acknowledging the implied compliment. The sergeant took a long pull from his mug, gazing past the foam to eye the men still milling around them. His gaze returned to Jim. "I see you left most of your share of tonight's beverage of choice for the other boys to enjoy. These guys may not be able to walk back to the barracks if we don't shut down the taps pretty soon. I'd have gotten us back to barracks a bit ago, but the brass is calling the tune here."

Jim nodded. "I'm trying to keep both eyes open for a while yet, if I can. I owe someone special a letter tonight, and my handwriting is bad enough when I am cold sober."

"That's no surprise," the sergeant remarked. "During drills I saw that you are the only southpaw in the company. I've yet to see a leftie with handwriting worth spit. But you manage to shoot your share of bullets on target all right."

"You got that right, Sergeant. Being a leftie doesn't stop me from keeping up with most of the guys in the field. And it sure isn't a handicap when it comes to running a farm either. That's what I would like to do after this big party is over and we are all back where we belong."

"We have that in common, then. I'll drink to it — and to putting *Jerry* back where he belongs. Speaking of that, I'm hoping we can get back to where *we* belong tonight before the next surprise drill catches us flat-footed."

Jim took the cue as a signal to edge towards the door so that he could make a quick exit when the men were dismissed to quarters. He wasn't kidding about those letters he had to write, and not just to Irene, but to his mother who still aimed to raise a ruckus and get him home. He had written Irene about his mother petitioning the Red Cross to intercede on his behalf for humanitarian leave. She wanted them to interrupt his training so that he could help his injured father. Jim thought, at first, that the Army might let him go back long enough to set things square. He worried about his father and his ability to run the station after his leg injury. His mother had even taken some days working the Texaco when no one else could pick up the slack. He knew his father would hate that.

Things were tough with no one around to collect the rents, work the homestead, or run the station. But the Red Cross would surely investigate his mother's claim. Once they learned Pop was out of the hospital and able to get around on crutches, he suspected that the Army wouldn't be too keen to give Private Hendrickson a break from his military obligations. He felt helpless, needing to be in at least two places at once.

He worried about his "Butch" too. She'd looked kind of puny to him on that last pass to Burbank. But he wasn't the only one to have a gal to worry about back home. One of the guys in his barracks had just read Jim a letter from his wife in Texas telling him that he was about to become a father. The fella seemed more frightened by the idea of his wife having a baby without him than going off to fight Germans.

It made Jim think. His Irene lived alone in Burbank with no family nearby. Would she want to return to Colorado to be with her own family when he shipped out? Could he convince her to move to Yuma so she wouldn't be all alone? He knew Pop would look out for her as much as possible. And his sister, Virginia, would help, too. His two younger sisters, Kay and Mary, still attended high school, but they could lend a hand once in a while.

The party showed no signs of quieting down, and one of Jim's bunk mates had already guzzled more than was good for him.

Lifting his empty glass in a mock Nazi salute, the man suddenly hollered, "I aim to drain these kegs dry. To hell with Hitler!" He began to stumble back towards the kegs with his empty mug gripped in both hands.

An officer gave him the once-over, and finally decided it might be time to dismiss the men to their quarters. On his command, the herd shifted slowly to the exits, glaring at the offending loud-mouth. Jim chuckled, wondering what would happen to all those yet untapped kegs of beer. Serving beer with meals wouldn't do their marksmanship scores any good. Maybe they could use it as shampoo. He'd heard that it made hair healthy.

Heading toward the barracks, Jim had begun to compose the night's letter in his head when the sergeant caught up to him.

"Jim, I meant to tell you. Must be the beer working in me. You need to report to the Red Cross community officer tomorrow morning. Is that about the business with your father?"

"My mother is trying to get me a humanitarian leave. Pop got dragged about fifty feet when a kid clipped him with a car at the Texaco station. He's busted up pretty bad and Mom says she needs my help at home."

The sergeant shook his head, absorbing the information quietly for a moment. "That sounds like a tough situation, all right." He sighed with a faraway look clouding his usually open expression. "Let me know what they say, yep? And good luck with it, Hendrickson. You're one of our best men, and I don't cotton to losing you from the outfit at this stage of the game. You're a good soldier."

Jim read the sergeant's coded words, knowing that anything referred to as a *tough situation* most likely would just have to be endured. His mother's calculated efforts to get him home, very likely, would not bear fruit. He had mixed feelings about it, for sure. His walk back to the barracks seemed a darker path to travel than usual and his shoulders slumped as his spirits weighed down heavily.

Later on, adding to his most recent letter to Irene, he decided not to mention anything more about the leave until he had his talk with the community officer. He would probably have to jump through some hoops to get the leave granted, but he decided he would try to make it happen. Maybe it would give him a chance to catch up on his real life before the Army took him out of the country. If it happened, Irene could join him in Yuma for his leave and he would try to convince her to stay there with his folks, so they would have some time together.

"And that," Jim said to himself, "is something this soldier would surely like to do more than anything else the Army has in mind for him."

Chapter Five

Thursday September 28, 1944
Camp Roberts, Calif.

Dearest Irene,

We have just finished breakfast and cleaning up the barracks. We fall out in 15 minutes for some exercises. Later this morning we will have some instruction on mortar firing. We are getting so far ahead of our schedule now that I'm wondering if this training is going to take all 17 weeks.

We had fried eggs this A.M. for breakfast. Sure tasted good after having pancakes for so long. The way they make them here, they would make good shoe soles.

As yet I haven't heard anything more about my leave. It takes quite a while to go through all the red tape.

We are having a little trouble with the goldbrickers in this outfit. We only have three or four that try to get out of their share of the work and we make it as tough as possible on those kinds of guys. Two of them are lead men from Lockheed, and were lazier then hell there too.

Will not get a chance to get a letter written to you tonight so had better get this mailed.

All my love,
Jim

October 16, 1944
Camp Roberts

Dearest Irene:

Here it is morning and we are all set for inspection. I spent until 11:30 last nite after I wrote you cleaning my junk and this morning they tell us that it will be a rifle inspection instead. Great life or what?

I just got back from another special duty at the Officer's Club. Seems like I get called for things like that more than I would like. But I might have the place to myself for a few minutes while the other men are still in the field.

It is our 18thmonth anniversary today and it looks like I'll make it to Burbank....

"Rise and shine, you slackers!" Jim watched in amazement as his sergeant barreled his way into the barracks, turning over every bed that had a body in it. Already dressed and ready for chow, Jim had hit the showers before starting a new letter to Irene.

In spite of the loud interruption, he smiled to himself. Sarge wasn't a bad guy, but every once in a while some kind of bug bit him, and he went on a tear with the troops.

"Hendrickson, what are you over there laughing at?"

"Nothing to laugh about, Sarge." Jim shook his head to rid his face of the grin. "Matter of fact, I just pulled a detail at the Officer's quarters and I will probably be on my feet for a couple of hours making sure they get well-fed, fat, and sassy. I'm laughing at my damn luck, I guess."

"How did you get tagged for that? I heard tell they needed a man from each unit, and I was looking to volunteer you when

I found all these goldbrickers still ironing sheets with their shoulders."

Jim figured the sergeant's anger with the bunk-dumping was staged. He was putting on a show to stir the men up. Jim had just written to Irene about the lazy fellows giving his unit a black eye. He and some of the other guys already had plans to give the guilty parties a hard time until they started to carry their share of the duties. Where they were all headed, slackers could do real harm to themselves and everyone else. They all needed to be able to count on each other. No man got a free pass in this Army.

"Let's go, you men. I want to see some shine on those shoes before you head out to march through the mud. You want to look as spiffy as possible when you hit the dirt trail." The bellow from their sergeant nearly drowned out the collective groan of the men. They began to comply quickly enough, but one or two gave a raised eyebrow in Jim's direction as he sat apart, observing the commotion.

The sergeant, spotting the questioning glances, nodded in his direction. "Jim, here, sacrificed his own share of the fun so none of you will have to miss out on today's little field party. Being such a good guy, he volunteered for duty at the Officer's Club. You can thank him later."

Jim reacted quickly to the chorus of boos and whistles from the men. "No way did I volunteer — no sirree!" He pretended to take offense, but he really didn't mind being used as a target for the sergeant's jibe. "I guess they saw me coming out of the showers and figured they needed the handsomest grunt around to wait on their tables today."

The soldiers, roused from their sleep so rudely, booed even louder at Jim's cocky attitude. In fact, though none would admit it, most of them would like to have been chosen to serve the duty at the Officer's Club, rather than go to the field for the promised "mud dog party." They gathered up their kit bags with a few more wise-cracks, grumbling half-heartedly about goldbrickers who "rubbed shoulders with brass hats."

Jim watched them prepare to leave, anticipating a few moments to himself before his own duty called. Making close friends rarely happened in the Army for these new, young soldiers. Most learned quickly how to roll with the unexpected punches of Army life. For men who were almost always tired and busy keeping pace with training and drills, they found that relationships developed sparingly. Also, the Army kept moving them around. They did not stay with any one group of soldiers for long. It was difficult to stay connected with anyone in particular, and it seemed as though when chance allowed a beginning of closeness, they would wake up to new orders and find themselves, once again, among strangers.

Jim had heard from home that a guy he went to school with had been inducted from Yuma. He also continued to keep an eye out for Hugh Wilhite. But every visit to a barracks looking for either one of them turned out as wasted effort. Wilhite should have been easy to find if he was around. His dark skin would stand out among all the white men in camp.

Jim liked most of the fellows he worked with, and they seemed to like him and would seek out his company, especially when he was trying to do his daily writing. Sometimes, he missed just being by himself, an unknown luxury in the camp.

The malingerers who had worked at the Lockheed plant were not men Jim had known too well back in Burbank. Part of a slightly older group, they used to brag in the coffee break room that they would gladly sit out the war building planes. Their skills, like Jim's, had given them dispensation from active duty for the first two war years. Unlike Jim, they hadn't tried to get around that dispensation to join up. Lockheed had cut them loose right about the time Jim was finally allowed to enlist. The release put them at the top of the draft list for service. But that, to Jim's thinking, did not excuse a man from doing his best and carrying his share of the load.

As the men trouped out to field maneuvers, Jim put his unfinished letter away and enjoyed a precious few minutes of quiet for himself, a rare treat. It gave him a bit of time to think about how he would react if his mother's leave request was refused. He was almost certain that would be the result. The Army had invested too much into his training at this point to let him go. Jim's mother would kick up a fuss, but that wouldn't wash with the Army.

Jim dug out the boot blacking and began to add an extra shine on his own shoes before he headed over to the Officer's Club. If he managed to finish his duties there early, he could get some writing done before the other men filled the barracks with their noise, dirt, complaints, and sweat from the day's labors. He smiled at the thought that, when he returned, he could go back to the pages in silence for a change while the dorm, still clean and soapy-scented from early morning showers, held its peace. He headed out whistling.

"Well look at Private Jim! How come you catch the breaks all the time? Here we come covered in mud, and there you are still in your Sunday-go-to-meeting duds."

His bunk mates' stomping and shouting brought Jim's head up from the paper. "*So much for a nice quiet letter to my wife*," he thought to himself.

The guys herded in from their mud party, and they were a sorry sight — and sorrier smell.

"What happened in the field? You all stink so bad, the CO must have sent you in so he could get a breath of fresh air. Whoooeeee!" Jim tried to mask his disappointment, not just at the smell, but at the unwelcome interruption to his letter writing.

A couple of the other men gathered in Jim's corner at the end of the line of bunks, stomping muddy boot prints on a floor that would now need mopping before lights-out would be called.

A tall reddish-blond-headed kid tagged, of course, as *Red* spoke up. "You might as well get changed to your dailies. They've called another drill and we have ten minutes to report back for the next action. Sarge said to look you up and let you know if you were done at the Officer's Club."

Jim snorted. "Dammit all, anyway! I guess I should have taken my time. If I'd hung around ten more minutes with the brass, you would have been gone, and I would have had the whole morning all to myself." He didn't expect any sympathy and, sure enough, the men hooted with laughter at his long face.

"Misery loves company, ya know?" Red drawled. "I suppose we could tell Sarge that you weren't back yet, but hey, he'd find out. Somebody around here would rat you out for sure, ya know?"

"Thanks for the thought, Red. What are the plans today, anyway? Are they going to teach you how to keep that red head of yours down under enemy fire?"

Red didn't answer. He just gave Jim a slap on the back and went back to gathering up his gear. Jim gave the guys a "what-the-heck" shrug, and setting the letter aside for later, began to change his clothes along with his plans for the day.

October 16, 1944 Part 2
12:30 Monday night (10/18)

Hi Butch:

This is the letter I started last Saturday and didn't get back to until after our weekend together. I wasn't expecting that pass after the field work, that's for certain! Am finishing it and sending it so you will know I wasn't fooling when I said I started one just before they pulled us out of our barracks that day.

We got back from LA at 2:30 in the A.M. and got up at 4:15 and have been out in the field since 6:00 A.M. The duty guys would spring a night problem on Monday night.

As you can well imagine, I'm just a little tired and sleepy. Have to shower and shave, so will close this masterpiece of a letter.

All my love,

Jim

P.S: Throw this damned letter away when you finally get through puzzling it out.

Chapter Six

Oct. 17, 1944
Camp Roberts, Calif.

Dearest Irene:

Received your letter tonight in which you said there was a possibility of another Hendrickson. I suppose that this is a heck of a time for him to show up, but it would tickle me to death. If it happens it will mean, at the least, a hell of a lot of trouble and worry for you.

We were playing "cops and robbers" again this afternoon. The brass-hats around here get more childish every day. They have a new ruling that no week-day passes will be issued except on Wednesday night when we go out on an all-night tactic problems. The few guys here that have their wives around certainly are doing a lot of griping about it too. I feel sorry for them if their wives mean as much to them as you mean to me. When I get those ten days off we will have to make some plans so as to make the most of them. Am sure looking forward to those ten whole days.

Mom sent me a picture of herself in a nice leather folder. It is colored and has room for one of you in the other half of it. Will get me one of you the next time I'm down. Mom H spoke very highly of you in her letter.

Good night, Sweetheart. I love you now and for always,
Your Husband,
Jim

October 24, 1944
Tuesday
6 A.M.

Dearest Irene:

Am out in the field and just received two letters from you. Darned nice ones too. Am going to see you this weekend if nothing goes wrong here. I have a detail coming up but I can probably buy myself out of that. Am already looking for somebody.

We are going to be out here until 1.00 in the morning but they tell us that we will get off tomorrow afternoon. If so, I'll give you a ring. Time is short so will have to scribble the rest.

Honey, about Junior, I like the idea a lot although, as I said before, it's kinda rough on you at a time like this.

We have been playing "cops and robbers" again all day. More of it tonight. I can't see any sense to it but they call it tactics. The instructors will tell you that they don't follow the same methods overseas, so what the hell...

Virginia wrote and from what she says we probably won't meet up. She plans to leave L.A. Sat. morning and I won't get there till Saturday nite.

Well Sugar, I see the boys stirring around so must be moving out with them.

All my love,

Jim

P.S. I don't think your letters are silly either, Butch.

P.P.S Here it is 2:30 A.M. and we are a tired little bunch of guys. Goodnight, Sweetheart. All my love for the duration and six months past forever...

Monday Oct. 29
11:00 P.M.

My darling Irene:
Here I am back in dear Old Camp Roberts. We got in about 2:30 with no trouble at all on the trip. We had a lot of excitement today that helped to keep me awake. We went through the range on which the machine guns fire (hopefully) over our heads, and then we fired hand grenades and grenade launchers. We then made some bombs out of TNT and nitro-starch and fired them. My ears are still ringing from the noise.

Have to go to the dentist in the morning. Sure hope they don't pull all of my teeth. We are scheduled to get up at 4:00 in the morning. That ten days is coming closer and closer.

About December first we ought to be in line for the furlough. I need to get ready for inspection and get some shuteye.

Good night Sweetheart,
Jim

There is a gap of time between this last letter and the next one my mother received. I ask her about it.

"That's right. He wasn't barely even able to give me a short phone call before they trucked the boys south to Los Angeles and set them on to take available trains across the country. They had to move quickly and find their own way. Service men could jump any train and travel free, but they needed to know where they were headed. When I last talked to him, he was still uncertain.

"I didn't hear from him again until well into the next year. I've often wondered if some of his letters to me did make it to Yuma, and then didn't get handed on to me from the address he would have sent them. It was a long wait until I found out that he was safe and moving fast across the country — and then on into Europe."

Their "honeymoon" of training camp ended without a chance to exchange a hug, but Irene remembers Jim's last phone call as a blessing she was grateful to have, with renewed promises from him that he would continue to write, even if he had to do it with a gun in his hand.

"I was laid low by pregnancy. Your dad came down on a pass before I wrote to him about the possibility, and I scared him. I had turned pale as limp lettuce and couldn't keep my food down. I hated that he had to see me that way. We didn't get too much time together while he was training. It was awful to waste it turning green on him like that.

"I bounced back right away and returned to work the next week, although I soon had to give up the job anyway. Lockheed didn't hold much with pregnant women in the work force. And there was your father, plagued by a mother who, in her turn, was plaguing the Army to send him home to her. Mom H wanted Jim to take care of her and see to Grandpa's work while he was laid up. The Army kept saying 'No Way' to her, and she would just fire off another appeal. I think your dad's CO got after him about it.

"They finally hinted that he might have a ten day leave — probably just to shut her up. That never happened. Next thing we knew, he was shipped off without the promised furlough home. I guess maybe the Army thought that some of the boys wouldn't come back at all if they had leave right before shipping overseas. Some families might have second thoughts about their sons' patriotic duty and try to keep them back on the farm and out of harm's way.

"You know, my mother thought I needed to come back to Colorado to be with my own family while your dad went overseas. I wanted to go, too. Staying alone in Burbank wouldn't have worked, and I knew more people back home than I did in Yuma. That just about set up a civil war between Arizona and Colorado kinfolks when Jim's mother got wind of my plan. I'm not altogether sure how it came about, but Jim must have arranged for his brother to get involved.

"Ray just showed up one day from down in San Diego where he lived with his new wife, Molly. He helped me pack all my belongings into the trunk of his sedan, and we drove down to Yuma. Pop Hendrickson put me in one of his small rental properties close to their home. It was that apartment above the garage behind where he and your grandma lived.

"My younger sister, Rose, came out from Colorado and stayed to help with the birthing and childcare afterwards. I am still so grateful Rose came all the way to Yuma. I knew nobody there. And your father's mother never did care too much for me. I was too strong-minded, and I didn't sing to her tune as was the way of the rest of the Hendrickson chorus. She didn't want me around at all until she heard tell that I might go back to Colorado carrying another generation of Hendricksons with me.

"I think it eased your dad's mind to have me in Yuma where he could think of me with his folks. He also hoped for a furlough, and if I was in Yuma, he could spend time with me before he shipped out. It didn't work out that way though. He never did get to make that last trip home."

Her pause here is full of long-remembered disappointment. Had Jim gotten the chance for a farewell, they would have stored up strength from the pleasant times to brighten the days ahead, while he prepared to ship overseas and she began to grow clumsy with her pregnancy. With a rueful sigh, Irene continues, "Pop Hendrickson was so much like your father. I don't know how I could have gotten through that time without him. Broken leg and all, he looked out for Rose and me. Rose was just a young girl herself, away from home for the first time. Pop Hendrickson, like all the Hendrickson men, was strong. They all treated their women very well, like real men do."

A soldier's journey across the country was far less organized than I would have thought for the workings of a military war machine. During his trek from west to east coast, Jim substituted postcards and V-mail, which he described as a "waste of paper," for the daily letters in Irene's box. I carefully placed these fragile V-mails and postcards, all about the same size and shape, thin as tissue, in plastic sleeves, separate from the letters.

Military postal workers took the V-Mail forms written on regular paper, reduced the type to an incredibly small size and copied them onto the tiny tissue to save bulk. Jim continued to write daily, but processing and the irregular delivery of mail, along with loss in the chaos of rushing to the fighting, left large gaps between whole letters while he traveled. Some of these were lost to the vagaries of time and sometimes Irene didn't receive them all.

As he moved from place to place, Jim was careful when he wrote to omit details that might have revealed his location to any enemy who might have intercepted his correspondence. As best I can piece out from what he wrote, he left Camp Roberts before he ever made it either to Burbank or Yuma for the promised extended leave.

The last letter Jim wrote before he left to fight in Europe described a rough camp-out off base into the wilderness surrounding Camp Roberts. They took their gear with them, and set up rugged quarters, rain falling down on them as they struggled to erect tents for minimal shelter. He still found time and space to keep his promise to write, but he notes that he had to do it on the sly. His last letter from the camp develops in increments over a few days, closing quickly by telling Irene that the lieutenant was calling for him as he cowered with pen and paper from a hiding place at the bottom of a hill.

Those who marched with my father came to expect his disappearances with pen in hand. His late nights in the latrine writing by available light after hours prompted amusement and good-natured teasing from his fellow soldiers. Mail call became sporadic once they shipped out, and, as the action sped up overseas, became a much- anticipated luxury for all.

His daily notes barely outline the interlude of his travels from California through the country heartland with stops mentioned in Cincinnati, a stay at Fort Meade near Maryland, and, finally a tour of Washington, D.C. where the full length letters begin again.

He shipped out of Camp Roberts with others who were in the same "wave" of men on a bus or in Army transport vehicles. They were dispatched to the train station closest to San Pedro, some distance southeast of Camp Roberts. Where the train took him, and who specifically was with him on the journey, goes unreported. But soldiers on orders could ride the rails for free by the time Jim joined up. A government provision allowed any soldier in uniform to catch a ride on any train. It was not a rare occurrence for a traveling G. I. to "bump" a ticket-holding passenger, and this policy caused expected inconvenience tolerated with good will by most of the general public, and viewed by most as their contribution to the war effort.

The Red Cross, who supported the soldiers some years before America joined formally, played a large part in providing comfort stations for the men along frequently-traveled routes close to the different Army bases near train stations. Somewhere along the route, Jim picked up USO stationery and many of his letters from this time period and shortly after bear their insignia on the top.

Jim would have started out with a fairly large group of men from his camp, many from his own unit. But as each set of soldiers competed for available train space along the way, some of the men admitted to have taken unsanctioned side trips of their own, dropping by any nearby home towns for a chance to hug their sweethearts or their parents one last time.

Most would catch up with their unit at the New York embarkation point. In any case, such side trips would have been designated as going AWOL. Jim did not take any side trips since neither Burbank nor Yuma would have been on the train routes. And so he and his Irene did not share a formal send-off.

"His letters to you pick up in mid-December from Washington, D.C. There isn't any specific address on these letters like on his early ones."

"No, there wouldn't have been. The boys had to be careful of the censors. Jim was very proud that his letters were never black-lined. He was good at saying things in a general way without giving away secrets to outsiders. But after he left Camp Roberts, there were no more phone calls between us. That made it much harder on both of us. We each had to go our own way."

December 23, 1944

My Dearest Irene:

Am now in Washington D. C. and it sure is interesting. We have a layover at this station and I've really been taking in the sights. I spent the greater part of this morning going through the Capitol building.

I walked into the gallery of the Senate and saw Vice President Henry Wallace start the Senate session. There were only half of the Senators there at roll call, but this must be a usual occurrence because he didn't seem to mind at all. They got to arguing and I left them to it so as to see the rest of the place. Imagine what it would be like to have a job that didn't start until 11:00 in the morning.

The guards wouldn't let me in to see the White House, but Eleanor was probably on a trip anyway and F.D.R. was probably having a conference.

I then took an elevator to the top of the Washington National Monument and looked the town over from above. The whole thing consists of monuments, statues, huge buildings that are very impressive, and it's full of uniforms. I darn near wore my right arm off from saluting. Sure is one hell of a lot of brass in this town.

Honey, I sure wish the war was over and you were here with me. I know you would get a bit of enjoyment out of the sights around here and I would like them a lot more with you around. After everything is all cleared up we are going to get us a good car and do some sight seeing. (No more trains please.)

It snowed a little here this morning and you need your overcoat to walk around in, but with the overcoat it's not at all uncomfortable. This tiresome trip is about over now and I'm certainly going to hit a bunk when I get there.

It seems like six years instead of six days that this train ride has lasted. We got to ride in a Pullman one night but they made us use the chairs, darn it. It sure seemed a shame for all those empty beds to go to waste.

Must close now and see if I can catch a train.

All my love forever,

Jim

Something tells me already that being away from you is going to be rough on this guy.

II: The Fighting

Chapter Seven

12-18-44
Fort Meade

My Dearest Irene:

Arrived here yesterday morning and have not had any time to myself yet for writing a full letter. I still don't know how long I'll be here. Contrary to what I thought, this isn't a Port of Embarkation; it is just a preparatory step. We have had a physical exam, and have been issued a heck of a lot of combat stuff so far. I don't know one guy in this outfit because they split everybody up as soon as we got here. We may get together again at the P.O.E.

The barracks here are nice and warm and the food is pretty good, but I am realizing that I'm a heck of a long way from my honey. That makes me have more of a grudge against the Army. The last outfit that was here stayed one week and I think that I've got about everything, so it won't be long.

They made me get another "G.I." haircut and it's worse than the one they gave me at Ft. MacArthur. They are singing Christmas Carols on a radio someplace around here and it sure makes me feel funny.

It's cold around here; though they let you wear plenty of clothes to keep warm. Honey, I was intending to send you a Christmas present from here but it looks as if I won't have a chance to buy one unless I get a pass out of here. Should have done it while I was home.

I have put in an application to have them send you my big overseas raise of $10.00 per month. It probably won't get to you for 2 or three months, but it will probably come in handy when it does get there.

Has Rose come out yet? Are you planning to go to Yuma and live? Another question that I constantly wonder about is how you are feeling? Sure hope you aren't sick any more. Must close and hit the hay again.

All my love,

Your Husband Jim

12-19-44

Hello Butch:

How are you doing this fine sub zero morning? Boy it got colder than Old Billy hell last night although the sun is shining this morning and it will probably warm up. It snowed a little last night and will probably be a White Christmas here.

We are still being processed and have about everything done except get our rifles and test them out. They tell me that I am going to have to send everything home such as handkerchiefs, sweaters, shoes, underclothes and even socks. Will send all that I can't smuggle through to you or Mom and perhaps they'll let me send for some stuff later.

Am in with a bunch of guys from Alabama, Georgia, Tennessee, and Brooklyn. Think I'll sneak off and try to locate my old gang sometime today if they don't put me to work.

Must close. (They did put me to work.)

Love,

Jim

Jim didn't think he had ever been this cold. And why did the Army want him to send home his spare changes of clothing? If he could get away with it, he would wear every pair of socks he had all the way across the ocean and on into Germany. Good thing his boots were too big for him after all. Still, his feet felt like two useless stumps of a tree felled in a Siberian forest.

"Hey, Brooklyn, how do people stand this hell-fire cold?" Jim bunked next to a man from New York who seemed unfazed by the frigid weather. If there was some trick to keeping warm, he thought he might just as well find out what it was.

"What's the matter, Hendrickson? Oh wait, that's right, you're from Arizona. You desert rats don't run blood through your veins thick enough to fight off frost. You're likely to break in two pieces once we get some real cold weather."

The Brooklyn boy had a friendly enough disposition, but most of the other guys in this newly-formed unit could not keep up with his rapid-fire speech. Like Jim, most of the men hailed from smaller towns further west, accustomed to moving at a more relaxed pace than these eastern people seemed to chase.

"I just figured it out, Brooklyn. You talk fast so as to get the words out before your damn-fool tongue freezes. But how do you keep your feet thawed out just standing still? Does flapping your jaws keep your whole body warm?"

Brooklyn just laughed. "The trick, my friend? Just keep dancing." Brooklyn executed an impromptu tap dance in his ungainly boots, worthy of every Gene Kelly movie they had ever watched. A few of the men got up and clapped and stomped with him. Brooklyn ended with a jazz-hands flourish and bowed at the waist.

Laughing, they returned to their packing, each one with the tough task of choosing what to send home or trust to the Army for storage. Orders had come down to rid themselves of every last thing that was not official Army issue. Most of the inspectors would close their eyes to treasured photographs of loved ones carefully nestled in a wallet, but the Army appeared determined that they would not wear one stitch of clothing that wasn't G.I. manufactured. The trick for today was to find a way to hang on to some of the comforts from home.

Jim watched as the kid from Alabama, the youngest and shyest among them, rolled up some hand-knit socks with a sigh. The sorrow on his face made Jim believe those socks meant something special to him; probably made with loving care by a sweetheart back home. Jim understood, and shared, the young man's feelings.

Directing his remarks to Alabama, Jim raised his voice. "You know, fellows, I think this man's Army is trying to convince us this war means we have to leave most of ourselves behind. Otherwise, why would they care about the color of our underwear? But I'll tell you, I'm putting my extra socks on my feet. I'll wear every pair all at once from now until the war ends if I have to. Lucky for me the Army gave me shoes way too big to begin with."

Alabama brightened up a bit at this and nearly smiled. Catching this with a side glance, Jim figured the young soldier hadn't ever thought about going against orders. He wasn't exactly telling the fellow to disobey the command, but he was glad the kid had gotten the idea. A pair of socks might seem a small thing, but if it meant abandoning a link to someone back home, he reckoned a lapse in military obedience was worth the risk.

Brooklyn joined Jim by his bunk. "You know the damned Army won't ship us out on Christmas Day, don't you?" Brooklyn seemed to know how things worked more than the others, or at least he acted like he did. He hadn't steered them wrong yet, though Jim wondered if that might not go down to dumb luck. Jim hadn't seen a cocky attitude in many of the guys, and he figured it must come from big-city living. "They'll probably herd us onto a boat the day after Christmas so we can lose our turkey dinner over the side and feed the fish in the Atlantic. Won't that be swell? Better go easy on the Christmas pudding. Tell you what, Sarge said to take these bags over to be processed. We have a couple of duty-free hours before chow. Why don't we just sneak out? I know a place where we might grab a quick beer or something."

Jim joined up with Brooklyn, Alabama and his friend Edgar, (the only one to have stayed with him from his previous unit) for an unauthorized excursion. First in line to drop off their gear for stowage, they hoped to leave the base without challenge and hit civilization, a short, but perilous walk on icy streets. Their New Yorker guide advised them to walk with confidence.

Jim just wanted to find something he could send to Irene for Christmas. "Guys, how about we split up? I don't feel much like having a beer. I ate three hot link sausages for breakfast a couple of hours ago and they just started to growl at me."

"Tell, you what, Jim, there's a small family store just around the block. You could get something to settle your stomach, and we can probably get something to wet our whistles too."

Brooklyn knew his way around the area surrounding Ft. Meade in Maryland. He led them out with no challenge and headed directly to a store where the owners, probably man and wife, welcomed them like old friends, obviously accustomed to soldiers dropping in. The store glowed brightly with Christmas lights and decorations for the season. A small collection of gifts and souvenir items from the capital city held pride of place in a patriotic display next to a collection of postcards and stationery. While the others went in search of something to drink, Jim looked over the items, keeping an eye out for something that might make Irene smile.

He picked up a small pouch. A mail tag attached said, "*To you I send this souvenir, with greetings warm and true, and may I add this line of cheer: 'Good health and luck to you.'*"

Humph, Jim thought to himself. Not too romantic, but he could write his own note to make the sentiment stronger. He had just visited the places shown on the small cards. This was a way to share the sights with Irene a bit.

The woman running the store stood watching Jim, a fond sparkle in her eyes. Her voice lifted with a musical lilt, catching Jim's interest and attention.

"Did ya find something, then, soldier?"

"Yes, ma'am, I believe I did. Could you wrap this for Christmas, please?"

"And where will this be going then, would you tell me?" Her lilting tongue sounded Irish to Jim, and her twinkling eyes told him that she had probably sold many a small trinket bought by a soldier to send home.

"This is going to Burbank, California, to my wife," Jim said proudly.

"And a lucky woman she surely must be, to have a fine soldier like yourself for a husband. Handsome, too, he is, to top it off." She laughed as she wrapped the small pouch in red and green paper with sprigs of Christmas holly running across in a pattern of festive frolic.

"I am a lucky guy to have Irene waiting at home for me. She will soon give birth to our child, and I hope to be there to welcome him when I get back from this party the Army is sending me to attend."

Jim realized as he spoke that he had not told anyone else about Irene's possible pregnancy, or his hopes to get home in time for the birth. He had held the secret close, away from the men he shared his quarters. Speaking it aloud to this stranger, a woman he had never seen before, somehow made it seem more real. Before now, Junior had existed only in the inky world of the letters between himself and his wife.

The shopkeeper seemed to sense Jim's profound feelings, and she gazed at him with eyes wide and clear. "I'll be speaking to the good Lord, tonight, I will, young soldier. And in my prayers I'll be asking a blessing on her, and on that child she carries. May you soon go home to see him grow up tall and strong and handsome — just like his young father."

Jim paid his money and took the package from her warm hands that touched his own with gentle strength. She rested her palm on his wrist for a brief moment and her eyes misted, sparkling blue with concern.

"I thank you, ma'am," Jim said, gazing back at her with quiet calm.

"And I thank you back, young sir. It's a grand, but fearsome thing to serve your country. And bless you for it too."

Jim joined the others feeling a bit lighter at this touch of feminine grace. He sure was glad to have found something for Irene. It was a small trinket, not very expensive, just a miniature mail pouch of pictures from Washington D. C. but it was something that would go from his hand to hers.

The men moved quickly as they headed back to base, only to find that they had missed the announcement of reassignment to different platoons. They hadn't had time even to learn much of each others' stories beyond where they hailed from before they had to shake hands and say goodbye. Of all the men he had bunked with these last several nights, only Edgar would go with him to the new quarters, and Jim felt grateful for at least one familiar face. In the eight days stationed at Fort Meade, he and Edgar moved around three different times. And then, on Christmas Day (in spite of the prediction from the soldier from Brooklyn), they moved again to board the ship filled with troops leaving America.

Jim's active participation in the European Theater began on December 26 of 1944, as he shipped out on the *Queen Mary* to cross the Atlantic, an ocean he had never seen, a detail he decided not to include in his letters to Irene. His company made their way across the water to join the American forces already well into the fighting in the Ardennes Forest.

The warm wishes of the Irish shopkeeper had given Jim a last spark of blessing from home to light his way across the gray waters on into the grayer snow, mud and contrast of splashed blood that were to become the norm for a while.

As he stared out at the endless water from his perch at the rail of the ship he wasn't supposed to mention by name, all he could think of was how far away he would be from Irene — and how much he wished he hold her and feel warm again.

Chapter Eight

12/26-44

Hello Butch:

Here is the great letter writer again making another feeble attempt at an interesting letter when the censorship regulation won't let me tell you what I've been doing, when I did it or where I am right now. As for telling you why we do things, as usual, it is beyond me.

Went out to the shower tonight and somebody had beat me to the hot water. Being a hardy soul, I jumped in and it was the coldest ten minutes I ever spent. Washed out a few clothes and am very seriously thinking of going to bed when I finish this letter.

Still no word from you, but that is to be expected from here on out. One of these nice cold days I expect to get about ten or fifteen letters from you all at once. Believe me, it will be like finding a million dollars.

I had a slight accident on the icy deck today. Really took a spill, but no damage done except for a little cracked ice and a lot of cussing. The next time they yell chow, perhaps I won't run so fast when the place is iced up. So much for the dreary events of another Army day. We'll see how many hours sleep I can snatch before they drag me out again.

All my love,

Jim

Would like to have one of those color pictures we took if you have them developed.

January 15, 1944
Somewhere in Belgium

Dearest Irene:

Am sending this in care of Mom because you will probably be there when this arrives. Needless to say, I have left the United States and am in the European theater. Boy I've done a lot of traveling in the last few months. Tell Mom I received her telegram and was glad she received my address.

I suppose you will have received my delayed Christmas present by now. I kept thinking that I would get the chance to buy something appropriate, but didn't, so I got mad and wired the $30.00. When you get the color pictures, I would like to have a couple of them.

Would like to tell you of the trip over and my experiences since I left, but it can wait until after this old war is over. The people here are nice and friendly, but you can't understand them much.

Am still with a nice bunch of guys and our C.O. seems like a pretty good man. Am being fed well and it is warm enough. We had fried chicken today. The Army sure is getting extravagant.

Did Mac ever show up? Would like to see the old son-of-a-gun. If you see him, tell him to go to hell for me, will you?

Though I'm far away, my thoughts and love are always with you, Butch. Take good care of yourself for me, and I'll do the same for you.

You said in your last letter that you are getting fat and I sure wish I was there to tease you about it.

Will write as often as possible.

All my love,

Jim

Jim looked the letter over quickly and shook his head as he sealed it. The things he had to leave out made the writing so hard. His topics jumped around like popcorn kernels on hot oil, blown up full of hot air and not too nutritious. He tried not to write something that would give Irene a reason to worry more. The men had listened to many lectures before they left the States, but the one topic that got covered so often they could recite the text, covered the realities of censorship. He couldn't give even a hint of their location, not that he had a real firm grasp of their position anyway.

His ocean voyage would have amazed Irene. The size of the *Queen Mary*, and the way you could look out and see nothing but water — not even a bird in the sky to break the vast expanse of rolling waves — sure made a man feel small. But that would have to wait.

It was standard that the ocean liners taking Americans to the fighting traveled with a protective convoy. The German U-boats were a dire threat. An officer had assured Jim that the *Queen Mary* was a fast vessel, able to outrun a German submarine. Jim figured he was lucky the water had stayed empty.

Just thinking about that frozen trip across the ocean made Jim shiver. The thin bunks had not offered much by way of warmth or softness either. When he had envisioned an ocean voyage, he had imagined a soothing rocking motion, like lullaby-time in a baby's cradle. Most of the rocking motion he and the other G.I.s experienced roiled guts as each man coped with a queasy stomach ready to reject food rations over the side of the ship.

Finally, the long-awaited sighting of land had raised his spirits until they faced the staggering walk down a gang-plank. The much-anticipated escape from the ship turned out to be a lurching descent on legs that wobbled, jelly-like to hit dry land below.

The pace down the gangway accelerated to a stumbling dog trot, with all worldly possessions hung in a duffle bag slung over straining shoulders. Even for those who managed not to fall to their knees, such lack of sure-footedness deflated their dignity as nearly every fella in the company struggled to remain vertical. Welcome to Europe, Americans.

Once on land, Jim joined Edgar and they looked around for transport. Edgar, still feeling the roll of the ship they had left, grunted shakily at Jim. "I guess we are slated to walk across most of Europe, Jim."

"Ha!" Jim replied, "Should have known there was a reason they called it the Infantry Division instead of the Cavalry or the Motor Division."

"To make it worse, I've never experienced such bitter cold," Edgar complained.

Jim didn't answer, but he nodded grim agreement. He had thought New York cold, but when his feet touched this foreign shore, they felt like numb chunks of frozen meat. The only way he knew his boots touched ground was from the sound of them sucking up the muck from the sodden earth. He spared a thought for the boy from Alabama and his home-knit, smuggled socks.

The long journey on foot began for the men. They would settle in temporary quarters for the night, sleeping rough without even breaking out the tents. A couple of nights, they had only their olive green wool blankets to stave off the cold. Jim was often the last one of the bunch still awake.

Determined to keep his promise to write every day, he used moments stolen at night to compose parts of letters. When the mail truck caught up with their camp, he would have a stack ready to add to the pouch.

Without a place to replenish his supply of stationery, he had resorted to using the hated V-mail. The form required staying between lines, writing small and cramped. His handwriting was already hard enough to read. The Army would then shrink it down even further, copying it on thin tissue. Jim figured Irene would need a magnifying glass. Stationery grew scarce, impossible to hoard. He dreaded the day he might have nothing to use. He also worried about what he would do if he ran out of stamps.

After four straight days of walking with just a few hours to nap between marches, the men had a brief rest before moving on again. Jim had no idea where he was in a world that had shrunk to the next step in the dirt in front of them. But for now, they sheltered in a barn set up with minimal cots, and it looked like the Hilton to the soldiers who had already grown used to sleeping on the dirt wherever the platoon leader told them to fall out.

Exhausted, Jim began to pen his nightly lines. A rustling groan down from Jim's cot made him wonder if one of the soldiers had fallen prey to nightmares. Some of the guys suffered a real rough time getting used to things over here. In the pale gleam of dim moonlight, Jim saw that the groaning soldier was Pop Adams, the oldest one of this group of guys sharing what the Army called "quarters." Pop, roused by his dreams, spotted Jim awake and gestured for him to join him outside. Jim took his cigarette lighter along for a quick smoke with the older man.

"Somehow I just can't get used to these luxurious beds," Pop joked as they crouched on the porch and lit up their smokes. "Folks this side of the water must not a-growed as much as American men. Or maybe they don't mind having their feet lop over the edge of the mattress at night. I don't cotton to it myself. My feet go dead on me."

Jim nodded in agreement. While not as tall as Pop, Jim's five-foot-ten-inch frame covered more territory than the length of any bed he had slept in since Camp Roberts. He could only stretch out when they slept on dirt.

"You know, Pop, I feel like I'm finally in the real Army over here. I hated Camp Roberts before we left, but now I wish I could bed down in the barracks. I also miss knowing that I could reach my wife in Burbank with a phone that stood just a few buildings down the path. I'll sure be glad when we get to wherever it is we are going and get the job done."

"I think we'll play 'hurry and catch-up' for a while now, Jim. I heard tell that we're headed to join a push that started a bit ago. Almost two years, this company has been commissioned. We're going at a hell-bent-for-leather pace, much faster than normal. That motor launch the CO described is strange too. I expected the infantry to be all footwork, and we've covered lots of miles in trucks. Not that my dogs will bark about riding once in a while."

Jim nodded at that, and it reminded him to rub his sore feet. "I thought I would be spending time looking for my brother. I think the Army didn't get that part of the deal."

"You have a brother over here?"

"Yes," Jim replied and sighed deeply. "That was the main reason I kept trying until they finally let me join up. Bill was shot down and he's in Germany in some POW camp. Hell, I don't even know which way Germany *is* from here."

Pop Adams spit on the ground in sympathy.

"I'm pretty good with geography, and it feels like the Army brought some of the men here by way of Scotland and some through France. My best guess is that, from here, we will head through Holland and hit Germany from its blind side. What do you think, Pop?"

"Your geography is better than mine, Jim, but from what I know of Army life, you can't bet on logic. If we do go further north, we just may freeze the feet off the entire division."

"I'll keep that in mind. I don't say much to the people in charge if I can help it, but if we end up in Denmark, you can bet I'll let them know that they've overshot the target by a good bit. We need to visit Hitler's front porch before we can put an end to this party, and the sooner we get to *Krautland*, the happier my feet and I will both be."

"Somehow," Pop continued as the smoke framed his face against the dim light cast by the pale moon, "I expected to see some action just as soon as we got off that ship. I can't help but wonder how our boys will fare in the fighting. Most of them carried guns, but just to shoot squirrels or crows on their farms."

Jim looked at the older man, sharing his concerns. "Well, sir, it's like I told the guys last night when we had to leave our cozy blanket in the dirt. What I plan to do is exactly what I'm told, go where they point me, keep my gun clean and oiled, and try to ignore that I am scared shiftless most of the time."

Pop chuckled at that and nodded his head. "I'll quote you on that line, son. Though I might not say *shiftless* the way you did. Strong feelings call for strong language. Let's just make sure that our boys aren't the ones to darken their drawers when the shooting starts in earnest."

The men returned to their beds, Jim to finish a few more lines and then fall into much-needed sleep. He still had his mind on how he could get information about his brother. He knew it wasn't going to be easy, and he had a strong feeling that they would be in the midst of battle very soon. Sleep came like a welcome guest, cutting off dark thoughts with dreamless slumber.

Chapter Nine

Jan. 20, 1945
Somewhere in Belgium

My Dearest Irene:

Am fresh out of air mail stamps, so must send this to you the long way. This is probably the last letter you will receive from me for some time as things change fast around here. For the last few days, seven of my outfit and myself have been staying with an old lady, 82 years old and she really has been nice to us.

I have your picture here in front of me and sure wish you were really here—no I don't wish you were here, but I do wish that we were together again. It has been a month and nine days since I kissed you goodbye now. Am counting the minutes until we are again together.

Butch, no matter what you hear, believe me when I say that I'll be back. It may take some time but don't ever forget that I'll be back. Time is short so I'll have to say goodnight for now. Keep writing. One of these days your letters will catch up with me.

All my love,
As Always,
Jim

One more letter was added to Jim's stack as word circulated that the clerk would arrive in a few hours to pick up the mail. He and his buddies were enjoying some brief down time in this nice old house they had drawn as billeted quarters. He looked around the room where he had been given a bed and all the comforts of home. Though aged and shabby, the luxury of the furnishings outclassed anything he had grown up with.

Photographs of two girls, probably his hostess's daughters, lined up in chronological order to tell the story of a family who cherished these girls from short curls, through pig tails, to long flowing tresses tied back in velvet bows; and finally, to photographs of both in wedding gowns, their locks covered with a cloud of some fluffy-looking material that shaded shy eyes gazing full of wonder from the double frame. "Twin sisters," Jim thought and smiled at the idea.

Jim continued to pace around the room, feeling a bit edgy after writing his last letter. So many things he wanted to tell Irene had to remain unsaid and he didn't want to write anything that would cause concern. He decided he had to go outside.

As Jim sat on the porch in the pale sunshine of the winter day, he remembered back to his first experience in Europe when they'd left the boats and set foot on foreign soil. He and his unit had sampled their first taste of fighting early on, and it was pretty fierce.

First they had boarded trains immediately, taking them through Southampton as the only identification Jim had seen on the quick journey through Southern England. The trains didn't stop, so they didn't see much beyond what was framed through the grimy windows of their coach seats.

When they got off the train, they got right on to an L.C.T. boat that took them to Le Havre, France. On snowy roads, colder than Jim had ever known, they followed trucks that carried gear too large for backpacks. The soldiers marched along interminably; already travel-weary and grime-faced. He had spent a good deal of those first days wishing he had signed up to be a driver for the Army instead of joining the infantry.

That first day of walking, his unit surprised a group from the German resistance. The skirmish that ensued left most of the

Germans dead, and those wounded had to be restrained and held as prisoners. His mind rejected the nightmare images that haunted him and he shut his eyes, refusing to let his mind back to that blood, fear, rage, and fury.

And now, like darkness to light, he found himself in a comfortable chair in front of this pleasant house, not remembering much of how they got here after the fighting. With time to think too much and a bed that couldn't soften his nightmares, the horror of their field work contrasted impossibly with flounces and plush pillows.

Still feeling antsy, he returned to the bedroom, still filled with the ghosts of young ladies whose fate he could not begin to guess. He feared he would despoil it further with his own demons. He hoped he hadn't let any of that darkness seep into the letter to his wife.

"Edgar," he called out down the hall to the next room, "I'm going for a walk. Do you want to come along?"

"No, Jim. Not me. Criminy! Haven't you done enough walking these last few days? Put your feet up and rest yourself!"

"I'm going stir crazy in here. I just want to look around and get my bearings a little. Say, if you're staying around, will you take this pile of letters? I would hate to miss the guy with the mail pouch if he should come early."

"Sure. Leave 'em here on the desk. I'll see he gets them. And best you'd better not be too long. If the CO comes in and finds you gone, he will likely take a piece out of your hide. Or worse, out of mine."

"No worries, Edgar. You can spin him a story and keep me out of trouble. It will give you something constructive to do while I'm gone."

Jim knew he should be resting, but his mind would not let him sleep or sit still for long. His thoughts kept returning to events he had lived through and hadn't had time to process. He relived the long walk that had brought him further into Germany.

Army protocol established a system of efficient movement of troops with ranks of men lined up in files on either side of what the people of this country called roads. Little more than dirt paths, they were barely wide enough for trucks and men. The Americans had engineered roads like these, finding the best way through the heavily forested terrain heading into Germany.

Each man carried his personal kit in a backpack, but tents and other heavier necessities such as food supplies and water rode in the trucks. Jim never had quite decided if it was better to walk alongside the trucks, where it might be a bit warmer, or in front of them where the terrain was smoothed from use. Following them was not a good option if a soldier liked to breathe air instead of toxic exhaust fumes. If any local vehicle or farm cart required passage, the men would squeeze off to the side in the snow banks dotted with dark, bare trees. Those same barren trees served as minimal shelter or targets when a break gave them a chance for a nature call.

After that first battle, the shell-shocked soldiers returned to the trucks. Jim's unit helped load the gear and clambered wearily on board, grateful for a respite from the noise, screaming and blood of battle. After about five hours of bone-rattling bumps along rough roads, the trucks rolled into a small village where a few short streets lined themselves with homes and a couple of small stores. It looked beyond beautiful to the men, and most of them began to rouse themselves from the stupor their first war action had caused.

Jim, staying behind to help unload the trucks, got separated from his squad of seven who would share one of the homes co-opted as their billet or quarters. The local civilians, willing or not, had opened their homes for the American soldiers. Jim didn't mind staying behind to help, but he hoped he wouldn't have trouble finding his bunch of men before they used up all the hot water or ate all the available food.

As he had walked through the small town the day they had arrived at this farm house with the nice front porch, Jim hadn't examined anything too closely. He knew only the name of the assigned house — something sounding to him like "May Zone Tee Bad Oh." The language he heard sounded like French to his Arizona-tuned ears. Other than fellow G.I.s, he hadn't spoken to a living soul who understood English. He wasn't sure how far they had walked, but he had figured this must be Belgium.

By the time the trucks rumbled off into the distance, all the other men had disappeared behind the closed doors along the village streets. Smoke from chimneys wrote unfamiliar words across a gray sky in darker smoky script, giving a sense of time past. Looking for his assigned quarters, he paused at one house briefly to look at the fencing, an odd construction, oozing up from the ground in layers of mud, straw and rock to form a small wall. The effect was surprisingly charming. It looked like cold weather, wet mud, and a bit of magic kept it all from falling flat to the frozen ground.

As he examined the odd fence, a woman had come out to her yard and called to him. Her words were unintelligible, but her invitation was unmistakable. She beckoned for him to come inside, hollering excitedly to someone from within. A frail man came out, rubbing his hands against the cold. He wore a huge apron over his dark pants and sweater. His smile was wide and welcoming.

The couple approached Jim and took him by the arms, chattering excitedly and urging him inside. Jim could smell the welcome from their kitchen, too. He had no idea what the pots in that kitchen held as they simmered away on a wood stove, but he knew it had to beat the K-rations he had shared with the soldiers on the road. His nose and his stomach decided for him, and he entered the small cottage.

The man poured Jim a cup of what smelled like fresh coffee, setting the cup down on a beautifully carved mahogany table. He warmed his hands on the ceramic mug and breathed in the coffee steam, anticipating his first sip with painful pleasure. He wondered if the slightly nut-flavored coffee was real, or if he had just gotten used to the freeze-dried field kit brew to the point where he couldn't tell the difference between coffee and something else foreign. But no matter, the hot brew flowed down his throat with welcome liquid warmth.

The woman, still chattering away in her own musical tongue, conveyed an excitement Jim could feel, if not understand. She brought a pitcher and bowl of warm water with towels to the table, and gestured for Jim to take them into a small area off the kitchen where he could wash up. Jim thought he had found heaven — but he carried his coffee mug with him to make certain it stayed real.

Clean from the grime of many days' march on the road, the warmth loosened the stiffness of sore feet and eased the ache of his muscles. Jim sat back down to a collection of dishes that he couldn't name, but the aroma and his hunger didn't allow time to hesitate. He took a huge spoonful of brown soup with what looked like a small cheese-covered sponge floating on top. The meat and onion flavor had a hint of something exotic, perhaps wine?

The sponge, an island of toasted grain bread, covered the soup with melted white cheese on top. Jim began to sample each dish, savoring the tastes of farm-fresh food prepared with unfamiliar spices. The couple stood until they saw him begin to eat with obvious enjoyment. The woman of the house refilled his mug for him, beaming as she took her place with the two men at her table.

They set to enjoying their meal almost as much as they seemed to enjoy watching Jim eat his. This archetypal breaking of bread together created a common bond as the three completed the meal in smiling silence punctuated by nodding heads. Chewing and grinning happily to each other like old friends, they made short work of the meal.

Soon, the woman moved to clear the dishes. Her husband turned on a radio and fiddled with the dial until he found a British Broadcasting station. Jim listened to the music and they all bobbed and tapped fingers in rhythm. When the radio started to play *I'll Get By*, Jim began to hum and then sing along, surprising himself that he remembered the words.

"*Poverty may come to me, it's true; but what care I say, I'll get by, as long as I have you...*" His mellow baritone voice filled the small kitchen, and his two hosts clapped and laughed.

Stomach full, Jim picked up his kit bag and thanked them, gesturing his appreciation. He knew he had better find his assigned quarters or his squad would be out searching for him in the forest. His hostess held up one finger and hurried from the room, bustling back with a photograph album. The pictures were of a young man in uniform. The tears on the woman's face, and the sudden quiet as her husband's cheerful glowing face froze into a plaster-of-Paris of sorrow, told their story without any need for words.

She held the album to her heart, and then hugged Jim, waving a tortured farewell. As Jim walked back out towards the odd fence that had given him pause, he turned back to wave his thanks at the couple standing at their door, the man's arm around her shoulders, both smiling bravely through their tears.

After that meal, it hadn't taken Jim long to find the place where he belonged, after all. It was just a few doors down and he had quickly recognized a man out on the porch smoking a cigarette.

"Hey, Edgar," he had called out, glad to have found someone from his squad so easily. He walked through a gate with the placard reading *Maison Thibodaux* and climbed the front stairs to the porch. Jim had found the men inside seated in what had most likely served this household as their living room. Cots lined the room where the men had claimed their own and still sat up preparing for sleep.

"Jim," said Pop Adams, "glad you showed up. We were just about to go out and beat the bushes trying to find you."

"Sorry to worry you. I got waylaid by a real nice couple of folks on the way here. I hope you didn't wait dinner. I don't know what we ate, but it was the best grub I've had since I left Burbank."

"Good thing," Edgar grumbled, "our hostess didn't knock herself out with any special hospitality. Madame Thibodaux is quite old, so I shouldn't gripe. Though it sounds like you lucked out as usual, Hendrickson."

Jim smiled at that, then stowed his gear. His elderly hostess had already retired, and the rest of the house held the quiet of weariness and fear. He decided not to dwell on the humors of that household. Not feeling like conversation, Jim got ready for much-needed sleep, and quickly penned a letter to his wife

And now, this next morning, he had left his recent letter to Irene with Edgar, and retraced his route through the streets of the small town once more. As he came upon the house where the couple had served him last night's feast, the smoke still swirled into the air. He didn't stop, but wondered in his mind if the boy in the picture from their album had known the twins from the photograph in his room at Madame Thibodaux's house. Who knows, one of the girls might even have married the young soldier from the neighboring house behind the odd-looking fence. He headed back to the *maison*, aiming to reclaim that chair on the front porch. If he couldn't catch a snooze, he would at least give his feet a rest.

They would be staying another day and night to rest. Then the squad got word to load up to hit the road again. Jim and his unit walked toward the clearing where they were to meet the trucks that would rumble away from town and guide them along on the next leg of their journey. On the way through the village, Jim, Edgar, and Pop Adams walked along the village road, he spotted a window box of small white flowers. One of the boys from Michigan told him they were called autumn crocus. Jim took off his hat and plucked several blooms.

Along the path, he found occasional patches of green growth, with pine and small cones from low-growing shrubs, a paltry yield from soil still winter bound. The frosty ground gave up a reluctant harvest, but the greenery finally filled his hat to overflowing.

He found his way back to the bungalow where the couple had fed him that first night in the village. He waved the other men along, telling them he would catch up shortly. Knowing that his dinner hosts had been through the worst kind of hell in a war started long before he and his squad had finished their training, he felt sad that America's arrival had come too late to save their son from Hitler's orchestrated horror.

He admired the spirit the couple had shown him in their generosity, and he stood in awe of their kind welcome to a dirty foreign soldier. He left his small collection of greenery next to the magically frozen mud wall as a last goodbye, a very small thank you, and a way for him to tell them, without words, how sorry he was that the Americans were so late coming.

Now, walking alone through a town reclaimed from German control, Jim wondered how many more stories he would see unfold of loss and sorrow. He decided that it would probably get worse before they turned around and went back home to America. He hoped he would also see other European families who had kept their goodly sprit and kindness in the face of war's devastation. He gave a thought to God that it would be nice if there were Germans where Bill was that would show him some kindness too. Then he picked up his pace to catch up with the other men who would join him in his walk through the snow.

Chapter Ten

In Belgium
Jan. 30 1945

My Darling Wife:

Again I am writing and nothing new to write. I have been thinking, as I often do, of our vacation at Pinecrest. We sure did have a good time there and am praying we will be able to have another like it real soon.

Our little apartment at 2117 A would sure look good too, with you sitting across the table from me, and us in the process of eating one or two steaks. I sometimes wonder how you could stand the steady diet of steaks I used to yell for all the time.

I have relived our life together a thousand times since I've been over here and find it was the happiest time in my life. When I return, am looking forward to buying a house and will have to see if you, Junior and myself can have as much fun again.

Am getting enough traveling to last me a couple of lifetimes and as for Europe, I wouldn't give two hoots in hell for all of it. They have some nice old castles, churches and monasteries, but a look at one and you have seen them all.

Am sure glad that we are fighting the war on this side because when we go through a town, it is almost always necessary to tear it apart. A window glass salesman will make a fortune around here after the war. The people here seem to be awfully lazy, but I guess they can do little until this war is won. Have only seen one place with running water and that was put in by the Americans.

The boys and myself are all rested now and ready to hit the road again. I suppose it will be real soon too, but I sure wish it were warmer. I think it is more my hatred of cold weather than anything else. The only time we get anything is when a truck comes in from the back area.

Must close for now, Sweetheart.

I love you always,

Jim

Feb. 23, 1945
Somewhere in Germany

My Darling Wife,

At long last I managed to procure some decent stationery. If you are getting my mail, it's been a poor excuse for it the last few weeks using just the V-mail forms. Enclosed is an article which you might be interested in though most of it is plain baloney. They seem to glamorize things a lot so people will even read them.

Say Butch, did I ever tell you about a girl I once knew some time ago now? I met this girl in a boarding house and after a couple of weeks I finally got enough courage to ask her for a date. I forget now exactly where we went, it didn't make any difference to me, but I sure had a swell time.

After that I was out with her until the wee hours of the morning most every day. About this time I was wanting very much to get into the armed forces because I felt like a slacker as most of the boys my age were already in. I took stock of what I had to offer this girl and decided it amounted to very little as I would sooner or later get into some part of the service. I tried the Marines, Seabees, and the Air Corps but no soap. I was "occupationally deferred."

To hell with them, if this girl would give her consent, we were going to be married. Surprisingly enough, she said yes. There followed a year and 4 months of married life which, for me, there could have been no equal. We didn't go out very much, but I believe we had a swell time just being together.

That's about all there is except that I was finally drafted into the Army and am now across the pond from this girl who has made my life well worth living. I expect to return in a few months and again find the happiness that was mine. Until then I will be counting the days and doing my best to get this war over with, and finally bring myself and my brother Bill home.

Hoping and praying that you are all right, I remain...
Your loving husband,
Jim

Jim headed toward the supply truck hidden in the depths of the trees. Word traveled fast out in the rough and if a mail pouch made it through the lines, word came across the ranks faster than tracer fire. He took his collection of letters, along with a few the other men entrusted to him and bee-lined to the mail station. One of the G.I.s from his unit caught up to him carrying his own collection of thin envelopes.

"Hey, Jim, it seems like you and me are the officers-of-the-day for mail delivery. That's a goodly stack you've got. Are those all yours?"

Jim smiled and shook his head at the young man who joined him. He had just written to Irene about this fellow soldier. They had seen some rough work together, and Jim considered him someone he could count on.

"No, Edgar, these aren't all mine. Some of the boys were too tuckered out to do the extra walking, so I picked up a few extra to add to my collection of fine writing."

"Know what you mean. Some of mine have smudges of mud on them. I think maybe the censors might cut those parts out in case old Jerry recognizes our position from the color of the dirt. If I do get back home, I probably will have a career as a dirt expert, one way or another."

The two men chuckled quietly, sharing thoughts of shoving some of that dirt back at the Germans. The memories of the last few days made them move with caution, looking for signs of landmines and other dangerous surprises that might lurk, left behind by the Germans they had routed.

The Americans could not wholly relax even as the enemy retreated in the direction they had come from, taking their marauding forces and screaming Meemies with them. The shrieking sound of those aptly-named shells as they blasted the countryside would haunt Jim the rest of his life, however long that might be.

"Anything real interesting you can tell your wife without getting it all black-lined, Jim?"

Jim thought for a minute about all the things he was leaving out of his letters these days. "Well, you know, I've been writing Irene every day and I guess she isn't tired of my belly-aching yet. Her last letter mentioned that my Aunt Hazel predicted she was going to have twins."

"You haven't mentioned an Aunt Hazel before. I have one of those, too."

"Well, Hazel's not my real aunt; she is my sister's sister-in-law if you can follow that string of family connection. The woman is a busybody, but I'm glad there are people in my hometown being nosy about my wife. Irene is down in Yuma, awful far from her Colorado kin."

"That's a rough one. Twins, huh. When is she due?"

"No, no sign of twins that we can tell. That's just Aunt Hazel being a know-it-all. She's a maiden lady and hasn't got any practical knowledge for making predictions."

"She does sound like my Aunt Hazel, Jim."

"Ha! I guess every family has one. Anyway, near as we can figure, Irene should carry Junior to the end of July. You think we might be done and home by then?"

"That sure would be a great thing. If we see much more action like we just came through, it just might happen..."

The two men fell silent. Each recalled his own version of the past few weeks. Every time he shut his eyes, Jim viewed a scene that looked like a still photograph, framed in his nightmares. In the aftermath of a huge bomb blast, a shelled tank sat, abandoned by the road side. The head of a Kraut looked at him through death-widened eyes, separated from its body by some now-silent act of violence, perched for an eternity on the smoking hot hood of an American jeep. Awake or asleep, Jim, deafened even in memory by the explosion, viewed the horrific sight in dread-filled silence. He knew it would visit him in his dreams.

He vowed to himself not to allow any hint of those memories to cast shadows on the pages of letters to his pregnant wife and he shook his head against thoughts of a son who might one day have to experience anything like what they had seen.

The two men walked together wordlessly for the rest of the way to the mail truck, grateful for the company of a trusted friend, quiet with shared experiences that they would just as soon forget.

Chapter Eleven

HEADQUARTERS 84TH INFANTRY DIVISION
Office of the Commanding General
APO 84; United States Army
5 March 1945
To: All "Railsplitters" (84th Infantry Division and attached troops).
You men can accomplish anything you set out to do!

At Geilenkirchen, Beeck, Wurm and Linder you drove through the length of the Siegfried Line. In the Ardennes you went on the defensive for a brief period and turned the advance of the German counteroffensive, then pushed the enemy back on his heels under the most impossible fighting conditions. You crossed the Roer River, broke through the German line and in five days time advanced 42 miles to the Rhine River.

In the advance to the Rhine you covered a greater distance than any other division on the line — through heavier fighting. After reaching a point only 4500 yards from the river, your direction of advance was changed to the north, giving you still another 9 miles to go. Without hesitation, you continued to advance.

Upon reaching your objective, after long hard, grueling days and cold, sleepless nights, you still wanted to push on, and asked for authority to cross the river.

You have accomplished what many thought was impossible. Without your drive and determination, without your spirit and courage, the drive would not have been accomplished as expeditiously — the credit is yours.

Once again I want to congratulate you for a job well done — a mission successfully accomplished. Once again I say I am, as you are, very proud to be a "Railsplitter."

A.R. Bolling
Major General, United States Army, Commanding.

Jim sat with a small group of fellow GIs, Edgar among them, in relative quiet, experiencing a welcome lull in the fighting that provided too little comfort and too much time to think. Some enterprising soldier had snaffled a bunch of C-rations, the kind that rarely made it to enlisted men at the front lines. The extra calories and prized meat portions didn't come in their usual K-rations.

Their perch on the raised hillock created a high profile, to Jim's way of thinking, but they had enjoyed several hours here, and the trees shielded them from danger above or below.

Mail delivery brought welcome letters from home. Among the long-awaited missives written by wives, sweethearts, kin and friends, today's mail call included a letter from their commander for each soldier, a copy of their own and one sent back home for posterity.

Jim read the contents of this unusual correspondence with sobering thoughts. He had already read his copy over twice, waiting for the rest of the fellas to finish. Jim could wait no longer, and broke the gloomy silence.

"What do you grunts think of this letter from the General?"

Pop Adams spoke first, letting his slow drawl drip around an unlit cigarette that hung, customarily, from his thin lips. "Don't know 'bout you, Jimmy, but this pretty much confirms my suspicions that the Army didn't think the bunch of us were anything but expendable. The major is a good old guy; we've seen that in the field on the rare occasions we get close to him. But he sure sounds surprised that he had anyone to write to after that last action we saw."

A few of the men nodded in agreement. Finally, the same enterprising gentleman who had snagged the C-rations spoke up. "Don't surprise me, none. The bunch of us got added on to units that started the fighting long before we got here. Some of the guys I've talked to who've been around longer said they decided to send us all here as a way to stall the Krauts, not push them back. No one expected us to walk out of there, let alone end up chasing Jerry across that line of machine gun barricades."

Jim wadded up the thin wrapper from a chocolate bar, a special treat in the field kit. He stuck the four-pack of cigarettes in his outside pocket, along with the treasured pack of toilet paper. "Well, to hell with that, boys. I didn't come over here to sit around on my duff and play eyeball poker with the Krauts. We are going to shove them all the way back to Hitler's front porch. Then we'll blow up his house."

"I'm with Jim on that one," said Edgar, taking his own bar of chocolate out, and snapping off a piece with his perfect white teeth. "We've got Jerry on the run now, and there's no looking back. It seems like we don't go two hours without taking more Krauts to add to our line of prisoners. And they seem almost happy to surrender to us."

Pop chimed in with his own two cents. "I had one of them ask me if I was a Russkie. I was holding my gun at his chin while he spoke. When I said, 'I'm an American, you crazy Kraut,' he dropped his firearm, put his hands up with a smile, and came right along. Turns out his gun was empty anyhow."

Another spoke up. "And what about them skeletons walking around in striped pajamas? I sure wish I'd a known they had death camps here. I pegged them as crazy folks, and it turns out we just liberated a bunch of Jew boys! Here I am over here looking for our soldiers in those prison camps — didn't expect the Jews. Some of them looked like they plain forgot to stay buried."

The men continued to voice their thoughts out loud at last. The catharsis of sharing made it more real, but somehow more manageable at the same time. Jim thought how one of these days soon, he might open the doors of a camp of soldiers taken prisoner, and his brother Bill would be among them. He sat up a little straighter and he held his head a bit higher with the thought.

Chapter Twelve

March 6, 1945
Germany as usual

Good Morning Butch:

I sent you a couple of cards this morning with a cute little girl playing with her doll on them. I sent them free so it will probably be some time before they reach you.

Enclosed you will find a cartoon and a couple of articles about what the Ninth Army has been doing. The article about the medics is good news for the infantrymen because the medic that we have in our platoon is right with us in every battle and they are shooting at him when they shoot at us.

The medics have Red Crosses on their helmets, but I think it just gives the Jerries a better target to shoot at. We are taking it easy now, but we are getting a lot of work that the M.P.s should be doing. Guess I shouldn't kick too much though because it's safer back here. I sure do hate guard duty more than almost anything else, though.

Contrary to popular opinion in the states, the German people seem to have plenty to eat, lots of clothes and are quite well off in general. They are sure in much better shape than the Belgians, French and Dutch we've seen. They did loot those countries and wreck their homes. What part of Germany I have seen, the homes are in pretty good shape so far.

Sure do miss you, honey. We'll have a lot to catch up on when I return. Must close again. Perhaps I'll have another chance to write again today.

All my love to you and Junior,
Jim

Germany
March 12, 1945

My Dearest:

Received a lot of letters in the past couple of days. You asked my opinion of a name for Junior. I would like a William in there someplace. My only hopes are that it is a boy, that he's a mean little rascal, and that he never has to leave as nice a wife as I've got to go off to fight some damned Krauts.

We lost one of the best damned Staff Sergeants yesterday I've ever had the luck to work with. It sure makes a guy wonder if this war is worth it. Something like that has a very disturbing effect on a bunch of men that are used to working together.

Sure do hope the old Arizona heat doesn't get too bad for you. I guess with a cooler it won't be too bad. Thanks for sending the note from Mac. Would sure like to see the old boy.

I received a small package from your sister Ruby. I guess she will get a letter addressed to Platner, CO, won't she? She had a pack of cigarettes in there and the boys gave me quite a ribbing because we get lots of cigarettes around here.

We are in another German village and it is nice and comfortable with electric lights, radio and running water. Sure beats hell out of the fox holes.

In closing, I will again remind you that I love you and you must take care of yourself for me until I can be back to take over that job.

Goodnight, sweetheart, it's been a long and rough old day so I must get some sleep.

All my love to you and Junior,
Jim

I see I'm still writing Pvt. instead of PFC on the address. Doesn't make a bit of difference over here whether a guy is PFC or Captain.

March 17, 1945
Germany

Dearest Irene,

How is my Honey doing tonight, or is it morning where you are? Have one lonely sheet of stationery tonight. Tomorrow night, we'll probably have a truckload of it, or none at all.

Received two letters from you tonight and you were on the dire subject of income tax again. If I were you I'd mail a letter and tell them to go to hell until I return. They don't need their darned old money yet and I don't want you to have to worry about it. Uncle Sam has given our family enough to worry about for a while.

Wish we would hurry and cross the Rhine and get this damned old war over with. They are working hell out of us now and it's O.K. with me if it will get me back to you even a minute sooner.

Less than three months now for you to sweat it out pregnant. I sure would like to pass out cigars as a civilian.

I received a battle star today and don't know if it's for the Ardennes Forest or the battle of Germany. It is most probably for the Ardennes because that was a rough deal. It was the worst time in my life. This has been a picnic in comparison.

It's been a tough day so I think I will hit the hay. Be sure that you and Jr. take care of yourselves.

I love you, as ever, forever,
Jim

Jim closed the most recently-finished letter and added it to the others wrapped for the mail collection. He kept a small hoard of his favorite letters from Irene in oil cloth until he had read them again and again. He made sure he answered each one. Once that pack got too large, he had to get rid of some to make room as new ones arrived. That felt like getting rid of pieces of himself, but he couldn't figure a way to save every one. There just wasn't room.

Calling the last twenty-four hours a "rough old day" qualified as a big old understatement. But Jim wasn't about to try to write Irene a letter that would introduce her to the unreal and inexplicable world of this war. He didn't have the words for it either, even if he wanted to visit that horror on her. No, he was better off just keeping Germany on this side of the ocean. Yuma and Germany needed to remain far apart.

He looked around the room that provided shelter in yet another German village where the sometimes-pleasant housing provided by the abandoned farms contrasted greatly with what he and his men experienced in the foxholes in the woods. With forced marches through forests or on barely existent roads between the small German hamlets, bit by bit, his unit moved, along with all the other units, from town to town. They took thousands of Germans as prisoners, establishing more "secure" territory with each battle. The cost in lives and sorrow grew each day.

Jim had received a promotion at the last General Orders. Glad of the promised hike in pay, he wondered what he had done to earn it, other than just what he and the other boys did every day. He didn't feel much like a hero when he knew he was just doing what he felt had to be done. He didn't credit the Army much with that either, it was just the way he was raised to be.

As a PFC, Jim had responsibility as part of a squad. Each of his current unit of only nine men stayed close at hand when possible, their major priority: look out for each other. If every unit did that, then all units would support the entire battery in the same fashion — and that attitude would travel up the line all the way through the entire division. The officers made the decisions from afar, and it fell to the NCOs to get the jobs done. That was fine by him.

Jim resumed his tour of the farm house, storing up pleasant details that he could share when he wrote to his wife. Writing the letters gave him a life-line out of this hellish existence. He refused to send the horrible and gut-wrenching accounts of war's grim duties back to Yuma, where Irene grew larger each day with their coming child. He didn't want Butch or Junior poisoned by the ugliness, dirt, blood and body parts that made up his days and nights.

So he collected a card with the cheerful face of a German child, a family still intact, people who welcomed Americans in their homes for a night, a warm bath in a porcelain tub recently plumbed with pipes for the rare luxury of running water. Not only did these niceties give him something to write about, it gave him a glimpse of bright spots in a universe that, otherwise, had turned almost too dark to tolerate.

Down in the kitchen, three of the guys from his unit gathered around an antique table, scarred and polished from years of daily use. One of his men sat smoking a cigarette; each had a cup of what passed for coffee, and the start of a card game sprawled lazily across the gnarled, but gleaming wood. Jim had watched as two of the men washed the dishes, shining up the polished board left behind by a Hausfrau whose fate they could only guess at.

"Hey, Sarge, grab a cup of Joe and join us," one of them called out grinning.

Edgar chuckled as he watched Jim's reaction. "I saw that, Sergeant Jim. You looked over your shoulder to see who he was talking to. You'd best get used to the higher rank, don't ya think?"

Jim gave a sheepish grin at that, grabbed a cup of the steaming brew that had been heated to sludge on the stove, and pulled up a heavy wood chair. "Fact is he just gave me another promotion. My rank is PFC, not Sergeant, and that's as high as I am likely to climb in this man's Army. With my raise in pay, maybe I can treat you all to an extra pack of toilet paper or something."

The men knew Jim's rank as well as they knew their own. Rank ruled the Army, separating those who could punish from those who worked with you, side by side. A man had to know who to salute, who to take orders from, who could be trusted, and who could send him off to die.

"Looks like we drew first-cabin accommodations for tonight's billet. And I see you are taking full advantage of food and drink that doesn't unwrap or come from a field kit."

"That's right," a blond, brown-eyed soldier answered. New to the squad, but not to the fighting, this young man added a fresh voice to their company.

"And congratulations on the promotion, Jim. I'm sure glad to be part of this outfit. Seems we get shuffled around like this deck of cards more often than we get a chance to play poker. And I sure haven't seen too many promotions lately."

Jim liked the fellows who were billeted with him. He had been lucky to have this raise in rank, he knew.

Most of the others tagged for promotion came from the group of men in the American Specialized Training Program. Begun back in 1943 before Jim enlisted, this program placed these ASTP boys in colleges all across the states. As soon as they shipped over, they climbed the ranks on a fast track, placed immediately in positions of leadership.

Some of them showed up and became what the men called "ninety-day wonders" with the rank to give orders, but very little field experience. Since Jim had bailed on the Officer Candidate training, he hadn't expected to rise above private, especially since he (and most of the other guys in his unit) had been attached to an already-established division. The 84th had been running around these woods a good long time before he had boarded ship to join the party.

Jim picked up his hand of cards and looked around the small circle of faces turned his way. "I don't know why I drew the lucky card on the promotion," Jim said, "but I sure didn't draw a lucky deal with this hand. Who stacked this deck anyway? I'll have to make sure he gets a double shift of guard duty when we hit the road tomorrow." The men chuckled at his joshing, knowing that Jim would most likely do the double shift himself if it came to that.

Jim's promotion did not give him officer status, so he couldn't order formal punishment, even if deserved. That privilege remained solely for commissioned officers, whose orders might include sending a man off to die. But a squad leader could assign ordinary duties and often used that as a way to reward extra effort and cooperation. Jim's way with his men didn't include asking them to do anything he wouldn't do himself.

The men played cards until they grew too tired to think, and hopefully, too tired to dream. None of them mentioned the staff sergeant they had lost earlier that day in the game of "cops and robbers" in the woods. They had barely survived themselves. The loss of one of their own to that forested hell hit pretty hard.

The slain sergeant was also a friend. But here they sat in comfort, clean for the first time in a week, enjoying the warmth of a well-stocked kitchen in a town that had been in German hands just days before. Their sergeant would not be warm again.

Survival often meant postponing grief until after the fighting finished. Those still standing would owe a large debt of sorrow to those yet to be mourned. But they needed to distance themselves from their grief today so as to prepare for tomorrow's fighting. The chair that would have stood empty was already filled.

With the last hand played, the men squabbled, as usual, about the size of the pot for the winner. Jim laughed as he handed over his share of the bounty, a whole dollar and a quarter.

"There goes a month's pay," he chuckled. "O.K., men, let's leave the German lady's kitchen cleaner than we found it. That way we can see to our breakfast early tomorrow with no complaints. We don't want the spirit of an angry German woman burning the eggs or brewing bitter coffee. We'll be walking again tomorrow. And I heard tell we might play dentist maybe find some more of those Dragon's Teeth to pull."

Quietly, with efficient movements as though from long practice, the newly-formed unit moved around the small kitchen, rinsing cups and cleaning out the coffee, banking the stove for the morning to come. One by one, they wished each other a good night's sleep. Jim blessed the thought that they had lived to sleep another night and face another day. "Playing dentist" to pull "Dragon's teeth" was no joke for the men. Their walk the next day would take them into the thick of the fighting at the Siegfried Line.

Chapter Thirteen

March 19, 1945 V Mail

To: Butch + Jr. with love. How about a date one of these nights? Soon I hope.

From: Jim, who is a hell of a long way off in a dump called Germany

My Dearest Irene:

Last night I wouldn't have made any bets that I would be writing to you tonight or on any other night, but everything went swell with no trouble at all except for getting a little wet. That was one time I was really sweating though. I think I'll quit volunteering for a while, because I've played my luck quite a bit lately.

Enclosed you will find that long-promised money order. I paid for a PX ration for the boys so it isn't quite as much as I'd planned to send. It might be enough to buy you a lollipop or something along that line. Remember the time you brought me the lollipops from Colorado? I think they are still kicking around somewhere in my junk.

I've received almost all of my back mail now except the packages. Received one today dated October 26th. Guard duty starts again as of pretty quick now so must close again and walk my post in a military manner.

Reminds me, they have a non-fraternization campaign on now. That's one thing that won't have any trouble with me on.

Good night, Sweetheart,

I love you.

Jim

March 21, 1945
Germany

My Dearest Irene:

Even in this place a guy cannot get away from the inevitable red tape of the Army. Today I had another shot for some kind of malady. I think I'll be so full of serum by the time this war is over that it will be virtually impossible to catch anything.

Am listening to Lord Haw Haw. He is certainly full of the well-known baloney. Evidently he is good at handling propaganda for Germany though or he wouldn't be on the radio.

Your letters are reaching me in a comparatively short time. Air mail seems to get here about 3 days before V-Mail. How does it compare on that end?

You mentioned something about your tonsils in the last letter I received today. Are you having any trouble with them? If you have any trouble at any time, don't forget to go see a doctor—though that is probably what you are doing anyway.

How is the weather around Yuma now? The days should be pretty warm now. How will you be able to take the June weather there? Maybe I'll be around and we can take off for the mountains. Am doing O.K. except for missing you too darned much. This war had better end quick or it's going to make me awful mad.

All my love,
Jim

"Turn that goldurned radio off, will ya? How can you boys sit and listen to that baloney?"

The men in the unit turned their heads to watch Jim descend the solid stairs in the house assigned to them. They had enjoyed one of their most comfortable nights in weeks.

Edgar nodded a wink at the others and they stood together like they had rehearsed it. Together, they intoned, "Germany calling, Germany calling," a good imitation of the phony British accent put on by actor William Joyce. The men liked to listen to the broadcast out of Hamburg by way of Nazi propagandists. One of them leaned over to lower the volume, but he did not turn off the sound.

"What's the matter, Jim, don't you care for the snooty accent from our own Lord Haw Haw?"

"I sure don't want to waste my time listening to him. For my money, he ought to be strung up as a traitor. I don't understand how a man could turn on his own country that way. Why the only reason he has a radio show at all is to pump people full of German *crapola*. It's all eye-wash."

"We know that, Jim. But when do we get a chance to hear anything at all about world events? With him, at least you know what is *not* going on in the world."

"Shame you can't find a ball game or some decent music to listen to," Jim responded. "But maybe I will be able to find some good music when I get over to Holland for that forty-eight hour pass the Army promised me. I don't know about you fellas, but I'm just about going stir crazy with all this lazing around."

The soldiers needed time to recover from battle and the physical toll on infantry men from the challenges of forced marches, bayonet action, bullets and bombs. The stress of flushing out Germans, taking them prisoner, and trying to clear safe passage for unwieldy tanks weighed on them mentally and physically. A sudden cessation of all activity and stretches of time with nothing to do but loaf around with their own thoughts threw them all off balance.

"Tell you what, let's find a spot that's clear of landmines and organize our own ball game," Jim suggested. "That would go down a whole lot better than listening to that yahoo on the wire. Instead of Lord Haw Haw, let's get some fresh German air."

"Tell *you* what," the newest addition to the unit spoke up with a grin, "we'll listen to Lord Jim instead of Lord Haw Haw. But how about you get us included in that pass to Holland? I sure wouldn't mind spending some time breathing air that isn't scented with Kraut."

Edgar looked at the men, waiting for the laughter to die down from the new fellow's wise crack. Then he said softly, "You know, Jim didn't get that pass for his good looks, don't you? Remember Jim, the fool who volunteered for some rough duty not long ago? He earned that pass. And I bet he would trade it in a hot flash and a flurry if it would mean getting across the Rhine and ending this war any sooner."

Jim clapped both men on the shoulders to ease the subtle rebuke of Edgar's words. While somebody shut down the radio, the new guy grabbed the prized discovery found in the barn — a baseball, bat, and a few old worn leather gloves. The men moved together, with the usual jostling and jollying along the way, hollering at willing soldiers from the other units to round out the numbers needed for a good game.

Playing outfield positions might make for some stinging palms and jammed fingers unless they could scare up a few more gloves for the ball handlers, but that was small potatoes compared to what they usually had to handle in the field work when the fighting was on.

Chapter Fourteen

March 24, 1945
Germany

My Dearest Irene:

Have written once today, but since have received two letters dated March 14 and 15. That is sure good mail service for over here. Thanks for the stamps, Butch, and also for the pkg. you and Mom sent. I got it about an hour ago and myself and the boys really piled into it. I feel like a stuffed elephant right about now.

Am sorry to hear that somebody swiped your first ripe tomato. I'll bet you have been watching it like a hawk for weeks.

I think Bill should stay home when he gets back to the states. He has been through enough to have a long vacation and then go back to a nice quiet civilian life. What a wonderful and pleasing thought. I've been trying for a long time to convince the Army that I'd make one hell of a good civilian.

So Old Betsy is on inactive service now. She will probably fall apart in a little while. She sure has done a lot of running since I bought her and she deserves to rest. Guess you did have quite a time getting her in that short storeroom the folks call a garage.

That sure was swell of Mom to go and get you those flowers for me. Tell her I really appreciate it. Am glad you had a good time on our anniversary and I guess the San Carlos Hotel did hold quite a lot of memories for you too. Would like to take you to a steak dinner there tonight.

Must close, sweetheart. It has been a long day and my sack looks like a feather mattress to me tonight.

Good night Butch.
All my love,
Jim

March 27, 1945
Germany

Hello Honey:

How is my Butch today? Guess you can tell by the news that all is going well over here. Was just getting ready to take off on a pass to Holland or the Divisional rest center and the Captain cancelled it without giving an explanation, so I might not end up being an M.P. after all.

By the time you receive this, I hope the war is over and done with. Sure hope I can see to Bill pretty quick and from the looks of the news that could happen in a short time.

When the Army does move, it goes pretty fast. You can never tell what will happen and if, at any time, you don't receive my letters, you will know that we had to move.

So Ruth wants us to have a girl! I still am voting for a boy anyway. How about you, Butch? I saw Bing Crosby in Here Come the Waves today. It was a pretty good show. Wasn't that the one for which he won the Oscar this year?

The news looks very good except for the Army of Occupation set up they are planning on. Here's one boy that's praying he doesn't get in on it. I would much rather go to Tokyo.

Haven't received a letter from my honey in a couple of days. Maybe I'll rate one tonight when the mail comes in. I think I'll go wash up and see if I can get close enough to the stove to heat some water.

Am writing on this strange stationery again, but it's all I can locate at the present. The stationery around here has its ups and downs, as you've most probably noticed by now. So do the men of this Army.

I'll take this opportunity to offer you a very Happy Easter. I'll try to go to church if we aren't on the move again.

Good night, Honey. I love you and I always will...

Forever, Jim

April 11, 1945
Germany

My Dearest Irene:

Am very sorry about the long interlude in my letter writing, but we have been moving so fast the Army Post boys haven't been able to get to us, so no mail going either way. There will probably be more weeks that I won't be able to send letters too. I'm still writing, but the letters won't get mailed as quickly. Please don't worry about me because the Jerries are scared as hell and don't have much fight left in them.

I have received a couple of letters from you lately and expect to get a lot more today as we are just now loafing around.

I may be within a few miles of Bill now. Have been doing my damndest to find out if he has been freed from here, but it will probably be a while after when you and the folks get word that I'll know.

I wish that I could tell you what I have been doing the last couple of weeks, before I forget most of it. We have captured and eliminated a lot of Krauts in the time and you should see the faces of some of the liberated Russians, Poles, French, etc. They are really glad it is all over for them.

I love you, as always, and am still counting days. I've got to get busy now so bye until I can write again.

Jim

Am in the 84th which is now with the Ninth Army. Tell the folks hello for me and take good care of yourself and Jr.

The date on this letter comes just before the date of the citation my mother has for my father's highest honor from the military. On April 12, 1945, he participated in heavy fighting, earning a Silver Star medal for gallantry in action. Irene kept the letter from Major General Bolling, the Commander of the 84th Division.

The letter arrived along with a package containing the medal and a description of the specific war action in sparse terms. The meager details in the citation were all Irene knew. Jim's letters weren't arriving often, and when they did, he didn't supply much detail about his part of the fighting.

Yuma Daily Sun, April 1944
Silver Star Citation Awarded Husband

Mrs. Irene Hendrickson, of 665 Second Avenue, Yuma, has received the Silver Star citation recently awarded her husband; Pfc. James W. Hendrickson, gallantry in action in Germany.

The citation, signed by Major General A. R. Bolling, states that on April 12, 1945, "when the advance of his unit was temporarily halted by intense enemy rocket and small arms fire, he left his place of comparative safety and boldly pushed forward in a manner that inspired the entire unit to follow his example. As a result the objective was taken, many casualties were inflicted on the enemy and a large amount of enemy equipment captured. The disdain for danger, initiative and courage displayed by Pfc. Hendrickson reflect high credit on himself and the armed forces of the United States."

My mother always said she never once feared my father wouldn't come home, but the last few letters made me question how close he had already come to danger. I ask her how much she knew about his movements.

"The Siegfried Line? You know I did read the maps published in the papers and accounts of the battles. And while I couldn't pinpoint exactly where Jim went at the time, I followed the war news and could guess fairly well where he had been.

"I figured your dad would be in the thick of the fighting. When the Allied Forces breached that line to march deep against German defenses, folks in the States began to think we might have a chance of winning the war and putting a stop to Hitler. We could feel an added optimism from the reporting, and people grew hopeful. His letters had that feel about them too.

"I still lived above the garage behind Pop and Mom Hendrickson's house. Jim's letters kept everything rosy, and I let him get away with that. I figured he needed to talk about something other than war with me — and he always showed an interest in the goings-on back home.

"I did my best to keep him up on all the gossip. I think it may have helped him keep his spirits up even when he needed to keep his head down, which I reminded him to do in every letter.

"One day, Rose came up those rickety stairs carrying flowers. Jim had written his mother and asked her to bring me some for our anniversary. Can you imagine that? He's fighting a war, trying to keep body and soul together, and he sends me flowers. Anyway, when Rose handed them to me, she said she darn near had to pry them out of Mom Hendrickson's hands. That woman complained that she wanted to keep them, and I was supposed to bring those flowers right back downstairs to her after I saw them.

"Rose told Mom H that the flowers might brighten me up a bit, since the stairs got harder to climb day by day and I wasn't getting out much. Rose also informed me that neither one of us would be taking them back downstairs until every petal turned brown and dropped down to the floor. Then the old woman could have the empty vase if she liked.

"One of the dried roses is in a scrapbook somewhere. You know, keeping the letters light and normal helped both of us, I think. I suspect that was true for a lot of families whose boys were away. Our world turned upside down when the Japanese bombed that harbor. People pulled together, for the most part. We talked a lot about tightening our belts when most belts still were cinched to the last notch after the depression years. But we looked out for each other. That's just what people did."

My mother couldn't give me any more information on how my father gained his Silver Star, but after researching, I found out exactly what happened through the memoirs of his Commanding Officer, Captain George B. Felton of Oakland, California. His daughter transcribed Felton's first-hand witness account of one of the most important battle actions in the area where Jim's unit was fighting, specifically on April 12, 1944. His account is shown here as published on the website called the The Lone Sentry. Captain Felton mistakenly remembers Jim's name as "Henderson" rather than Hendrickson, a fairly common error.

The next day, April 12, we started off smoothly about 10 A.M. Our other trucks had been taken away so we now had weasels and ducks (both could float) as well as trucks, tanks, jeeps and tank destroyers. We moved northward into the British zone. One small village had had a fine department store. The town had been taken the day before and nothing happened.

An old bearded Jewish man (one of two I saw in Germany) even stood and watched as the two or three hundred scavengers looked through what remained. The English told us about it and how it had started but the Polish were our allies and they wouldn't stop them. On and on wherever bridges could be found. Past an oil field that was bombed to the extent that it was hard to find a roadway between the craters. Toward night the column stopped. Sleep in the trucks or on the ground. I slept on the ground.

As we looked down the road to the woods we could see the enemy soldiers. So far, only two shots had been fired both by the tank. At a time like this neither side is particularly anxious to get the shooting started. In a column of twos down each row of trees we went — third platoon leading. Four T.D.s (same as tanks) moved along also. As we got within about 100 yards of the woods the T.D.s stopped. They wouldn't go any further until the infantry cleared the woods. I was about the twelfth person back on the right file. All of a sudden a panzer Faust was fired from the woods. It missed! A Nebelwerfer opened up with six rounds from 600 yards off to the left. All the rounds were just over the trees — boy that was luck!

The machine guns on the T.D. raked the woods. We all fired — at no target in particular. "Move on" I yelled. No one went. Finally, from right in front of me, Henderson yelled, "Hell, if they won't go, I will". That was all it needed. More jumped up and in a jiffy we were in the woods and capturing or chasing after the Germans. (They were not front line solders — more like artillery men.)

On we moved past killed and injured (a couple of each) to a motor park. We searched the area — rounded up 30 prisoners and six or eight trucks, a couple motorcycles and seven Nebelwerfers. Not a person was injured. It was a most successful day's work. We learned that we had caught them entirely unawares for all had expected the attack from the opposite direction and we caught them from the rear.

They couldn't fire their weapons at us then as they were still preparing their defense. S.S. troops were supposed to be to their front. We had done someone a good turn by knocking this unit out. We brought what trucks would run into Steinhorst and I left a squad to guard them. We took off toward the head of the column. 'E' and 'F' had been stopped at a crossroads only a couple miles down the road. A couple men were killed by an enemy tank. They had all had to get off their trucks so when Hardesty saw me, he said for me to lead off. "My luck can't last forever," I thought.

Before long — a mile or two — the small village ahead looked very suspicious. We looked and looked — should we go in firing for cover? No — but with all weapons cocked we moved on in. What in the world? About 300 fine looking young Hungarian boys fourteen years old were here going to a school about the German antiaircraft (88) gun. They had about eight German soldiers as instructors.

Col. Hardesty treated them all as prisoners. We moved on. At the edge of the village a shadow flashed past a barn door. I radioed back — it looked suspicious — a couple of Germans and 200 Russian and Polish prisoners were in there. When they were liberated they administered a terrific beating to the guards. On and on.

On and on until we pulled up about four miles southeast of Salswedel — picking up prisoners all the way. We had thought this would be the goal for the day but orders came to push on to the Elbe. I thought, as did the others, we would never make it. We never dreamed we were anywhere near there for our well armed column of 100 vehicles was snaking along at 20 miles per hour as silently as a truck. Arendsee ahead — big town — lake on one side. That is where they will defend. Steadily we approached. 11:30 A.M on Saturday — no shooting but all guns cocked as we rounded a curve and looked down the main street. Hundreds of people and many soldiers — "Hande hoch!" (hands up) I yelled. They looked at this column and bicycles, carts, kids and old folks scattered and ran as they took out white handkerchiefs.

Jim's next letter is dated as the very day of his participation in the action Felton describes. Even during this dangerous time, he somehow managed to find time to write to my mother. It's as though what he experienced that day is what passed for ordinary in his German life.

His letter contrasts so dramatically from the memoir of Captain Felton. I can only guess at what else is left out in his version of wartime in Europe. Like so many others who fought in World War II, their experiences remain hidden from our view, and we have mere glimpses from those who survived and, years later, are able to tell what they remember. I am so grateful for Captain Felton's survival of the war, and to his daughter for writing down his memories.

Chapter Fifteen

April 12, 1945
Germany

My Dearest:

Received your letters of March 2 and 3 today. Nice going for the mail service. Enclosed is a snapshot of five of our boys. The fellow who had the camera said it took 4 months to get the picture back. Taylor, Kelly and White were with me on our boat ride across the Rhine. The picture was taken when we were on the other side of the Roer River.

Butch, I just received the letter saying you had gotten the flowers. Guess Hazel Lawler must look screwy as hell with her teeth out. She could stand a little overhauling all over in my estimation. (I sound like a catty old creature, don't I?)

You sound like an old woman when you refer to your "younger" days. If my memory is correct, you are exactly 22 years and 155 days old today. We are both young enough to have one hell of a lot of fun when I return. By the way, what are you doing the first night I return? How's about a date for a movie or something?

Still have the two harmonicas I brought over and they sure came in handy in the foxholes. I've gotten another added to my collection from a German music store. Where is Bill Rohrer now? Is he across yet? Am sorry to hear that Bob flunked out as a pilot. He is a good kid.

Am thinking of volunteering for the Pacific Theater if they will let me come home right away. It might be a foolish thing to do but I might be stuck here for awhile if I don't. Write and let me know how you feel about it. They say the Japs are tough, but a bullet can get any of them and the Jerries are smarter than the Japs so there wouldn't be much danger.

Must close, Sugar. Remember I love you and will try my damndest to get home as soon as possible.

All my love,

Jim

Though Jim hadn't thought as much about his brother Bill for a while, suddenly he could think of little else. He and his unit were enjoying another brief respite from heavy fighting, staying in a rambling and pleasant farm house. This place had plenty of room on the outskirts of a small hamlet. Ample food made it even better.

But the expected warm welcome to a billeting was proving not to be the case in this instance. It had been Jim's experience that most of the German farm owners and small businesses in the conquered villages and towns he and his men entered showed relief when the Americans appeared. More often, they saw no sign of any Germans at all. It was as though they had evaporated like a desert rain above the sand.

Their hostess in this rambling farm house remained oddly distant and aloof, and Jim wondered why. Frau Hilda didn't treat them with any kind of specific cruelty, but she seemed fearful and resentful of their presence. It made Jim wonder why she stayed on. Perhaps she had nowhere else to go.

Many of the smaller villages, while not military targets, had been under siege by their own government for a long time, forced to supply German troops with what little they had from already meager resources. The Americans brought protection and order with them, and in return, the few townspeople they did see were usually hospitable and generous, especially for Jim's squad who tried so hard to be good guests.

The German woman's wariness with the Americans concerned all of the men. She provided for their basic needs, but remained unresponsive. Attempts to jolly her into conversation were rebuffed with silence. She seemed to cringe as she watched them consume the fresh loaves of bread from her table. They did not want her to be afraid of them. All the soldiers hungered, not just for fresh food from a woman's kitchen, but for human warmth, especially of the female kind.

Jim and Edgar, early risers among the squad, headed to the kitchen on their second morning, determined to charm some light from their hostess. She served them coffee in stony silence, then left the kitchen without a word or acknowledgement, heading towards the barn. Jim looked at Edgar.

"Looks like Frau Hilda can't stand to watch us eat. Why don't we finish up here and go offer her some help with the farm chores? That might be a chance to win her over."

Looking for her through the window as they washed their dishes, they saw her leave the barn, headed out away from the house. She carried a large basket covered with a cloth, and walked west across her farm land. The basket dragged her arms with the weight of the load and she struggled forward with determination. The two men quickly stacked their plates and left the kitchen to follow her.

They caught sight of her again as she left her property heading away from town. She looked around furtively, but didn't spot the two men in the shadows of the trees lining the boundary between her property and woodlands. They continued to trail after her as she turned off the path into dense trees deep in the forest. Curious about her secretive movements, they kept quiet and followed at a distance, hoping they weren't heading into a nest of German soldiers not yet swept up as prisoners.

The men continued silently and intently for about ten minutes, their prey still unaware of her followers. A clearing in the trees revealed, not a house, but a camp-like compound erected roughly over the ground surrounded by the tall trees. The rushing of a small stream masked their movements as they caught up within speaking range of the farm woman. Jim and Edgar watched their reluctant hostess enter the compound and looked at each other with grave concern. Then they quickly headed back the way they had come.

Once out of range of being overheard, Jim whispered to Edgar. "You head on back to the base, and I'll round up our guys."

Edgar headed back to command post to report the sighting of what they thought must be an enemy encampment. Jim headed back to the farm house and gathered his squad. Together, they staked out the perimeter, closing in with weapons to survey what they faced. There were no German guards anywhere near the prison.

What they found when they entered the compound surprised everybody. They watched from a distance as Frau Hilda had set her basket down in a clearing that appeared to be an outdoor kitchen of sorts. She pumped water piped from the stream into a large cooking pot and a fire put the pot to boil. She took a bag of oats out of her basket and poured it all into the hot water, then took apples from the basket and cut them into the boiling pot to flavor the porridge. A milk can sat, waiting to be added to the cooked oats.

The compound was silent, save for the clattering of her utensils as she focused on her work. Jim could see a few benches forming a dining area, large enough to seat twenty to thirty people. A horseshoe shape of what looked like horse stalls framed the clearing on three sides. Each stall had a barred door with only a square opening to allow fresh air. He realized he was looking at a small prisoner of war camp. But where were the guards? And why was the barracks so quiet?

Evidently, the German woman cooked for the camp. She had risked her own safety to make what she thought was a clandestine trip through the forest to feed the camp occupants. Evidently not bothered by the absence of guards, she remained also unaware that she had been followed by her American guests.

Jim entered the camp and demanded that she explain. "Frau Hilda, what is going on here?"

Startled to find him beside her, she gasped in surprise. Then she sighed deeply and spoke quickly, in a rush of stammered words. "I found guards already gone this morning," she claimed. "I told commander... Americans at my farm house.... He said to me, 'Don't come again.' But I must come. Men hungry. No guards here…"

Jim thought a minute. "They must have decided to leave, maybe to join up with German forces close by. Are the prisoners in those stalls?"

Frau Hilda just looked at him, emptied of energy, obviously afraid of what might be found behind the barred doors.

Jim gestured to his squad to join him. He and Edgar exchanged glances, fearful of what they would find in the noiseless prisons. Jim shuddered, giving a quick thought to his brother, Bill. He cautioned the men to stay alert, and headed to the closest enclosure, raising the plank of wood that barred the door shut. When he opened it, the smell of fear and unwashed human nearly knocked him down. He peered into the room, expecting the worst.

On a flimsy cot sat a man wrapped in a filthy quilt. His hand shielded his blue eyes from the sudden intrusion of light into his cramped quarters. He stood slowly, attempting a shaky salute as he saw the American uniform and breathed a rusty, "Thank God."

Jim called to his squad to open the other stalls. The freed prisoners seemed weak and confused, thin and dirty, but not too unhealthy otherwise. All but one was able to shuffle slowly into the light and find his way to the benches where Frau Hilda had returned to her cooking.

Jim figured that questioning could wait until they got some water and nourishment in them. They made short work of the porridge cooked with apples Frau Hilda served, along with two loaves of bread that looked just like the ones she had grudgingly fed to Jim's unit the evening before. Jim now wished they had done without the bread so there would be more for these starved men.

The man Jim had released first told him that he had overheard Frau Hilda speaking to the Germans.

"She's telling the truth," he said. "The guards left soon after she did, locking us all up and leaving some bread and water in our stalls. Then it became very silent here, along with the night and the cold. I feared that no one would find us and just decided to sleep until I didn't wake up any more." His voice dropped and so did his shamed eyes as he added, "There was no way to get to the latrine. I figured we would starve to death or choke on our own filth before anyone came to find us."

Jim looked at him with sympathy and curiosity. The man looked familiar. He was about Jim's height and he spoke in a manner that seemed like home to Jim. But this wasn't his brother, Bill. His brother was in a prison camp under the watch of the Red Cross. That's how the family was able to get letters back and forth to him. Bill's *Stalag* was called "The Country Club" by the men there. This place was sure no luxury spot. Yet he felt restive and a bit queasy. The man he had just listened to reminded him so very much of his brother. He asked, "What's your name, soldier, and where do you come from?"

"No one has asked me for my name for a long time without hearing my rank and serial number with it. My name is William Arthur Rogers and I'm from Phoenix, Arizona. And I'd like to shake your hand and say thank you for chasing those Krauts out of here."

Jim's own blue eyes blurred a bit as the two men clasped hands.

Jim had heard about other camps liberated as the Americans had traveled through the war-ravaged towns and farm villages. This, though, was a first-time experience for him and for the rest of his unit. The prisoners seemed dazed and disaffected, some weeping to realize that they were free. Others were numb from the days of deprivation and years of captivity. They were a mix of twenty-two soldiers, some British and some American. For them, the war was finally over and they would soon be going home.

The process of questioning each one made Jim think again of his brother Bill. He studied each man's thin face carefully as the tired and dirty prisoners shambled out of their rough quarters. It would take a while for them to trust their freedom and absorb the fact that they would soon be returning home. Edgar arrived with the team who would handle the resettlement of the liberated soldiers. Transportation would soon arrive to take them to processing centers and expedite their journey home.

As Jim looked each man in the eye and spoke to him, Bill's face did not appear among the weary and bedraggled men, and Jim's spirits drooped a bit. He would have to be content liberating William from Phoenix for the moment. But he held on to the hope that somewhere, someday, gates would open for his brother.

How nice to think that some sturdy German housewife would have set out from her farm with fresh eggs and bread to feed Bill, as this German woman had done for these men. As for Frau Hilda, no charges would be pressed against her, but neither would she be honored for her brave deeds. She seemed merely eager to return to her home. Jim was glad she had a home that she could return to and he gave a thought to bless her as she scurried back through the woods.

For the first time, he considered the possibility that he might not be the one who would free Bill from his prison. He still wished faintly that, one day, he would stumble across a camp like this one with Bill in it. Then they could both head home together. After all, that's why he had joined up and gotten himself into this mess in the first place.

Chapter Sixteen

Germany
April 15, 1945

Dear Irene:

Received a lot more letters from you and Mom. Have been busier than a Billy Goat in a trash pile since the last of March. I'm doing swell and am in good health.

We captured Hanover a while back and it was an easy job. There is still a little fighting to be done but not too much rough stuff any more. Am still hoping for my return home by June 23rd.

I received the picture of Kathy that Mom sent and sure think she's O.K. If Junior turns out to be Junior Miss, I think Virginia Lee would be a darned good name.

Not much new honey. I'd better quit this if I expect to get it mailed.

All my love,

Jim

P.S. Tell everybody I'll write as soon as possible...

"Damn it all," Jim exclaimed. He watched the mail truck rumble away through the trees at a fast clip and cursed his luck. If he hadn't rustled around futilely for those few frantic moments searching, without success, for stamps, he would have made it to the truck in good time.

This sleeping rough sure was hard on a fellow, living out of a field pack, wishing for a bath tub with hot water and a scrub brush. Writing to Irene, today of all days, was a bit more than a miracle considering what he and his men had just experienced.

Turning his thoughts away from that kind of reflection, Jim folded the day's letter away carefully for the next pick-up, organized his pack, including the wayward stamps, and sat back down using a tree for a back rest. He needed to keep his thoughts occupied, and so he took out a packet of pictures from Irene's most recent letter.

He picked up the photograph of baby Kathy, Bill's first-born daughter. The infant smiled up at him from a background of sunny Arizona desert sky, an indictment of contrast to the gray and still-wintry expanse of chilly gloom that hovered over the soldiers in the German forest. Jim wondered if the trees themselves had soaked up the horror of screaming missiles, Panzer tank explosions, and cries of men wounded by artillery or fellow human hand.

Jim found it impossible to connect these recent horrors with what it would feel like to hold a baby in his arms. The baby girl's smile faded away as he reflected back on his long march through the snow and into Germany — and he nodded his head once as if in agreement with the gods who spared children from suffering in this place in time. He mouthed a quiet blessing for baby Kathy, and a prayer that Bill would soon be home to hold his daughter safely in his arms.

Nestling more comfortably against his tree trunk, Jim allowed himself to think again about the wonderful forty-five-day leave offered to soldiers willing to sign up to go to the Pacific and extend their Army service. It would mean two additional years in the military, but it would guarantee — or as much a guarantee as Army promises go — a chance to travel home and see his wife before he shipped over for more war in the Pacific.

His expected child, due in mid-July, should, by rights, be able look up and see a father standing by the bassinette. Jim would sure like to make that happen, even if it meant lengthening his military obligation.

He and Irene decided that Junior would carry the family name of his father and grandfather. A son would carry the name, James William Hendrickson, III. If Junior turned out to be a female, Virginia Lee Hendrickson sounded good to him. Both names had strength, and since he knew he couldn't get away with naming her Butch, he still continued to tease Irene with that suggestion a time or two.

Jim suspected that his own mother had given little enough thought to names for her children. His older brother, Ray, the first-born son, should, by tradition, have been given the James William moniker. What if all the other children had been born female? But she didn't bestow that name until her third son came along. That gave Jim a sense of pride. It would be a legacy he and Irene could pass along to the next generation of Hendricksons, and it seemed right to respect the tradition.

When Bill appeared, he had been named him William Clarence, giving him the family middle name as a first name. Jim thought of his brother Bill often. In the last few letters, Irene and his mother both described how Skee, Bill's wife, traveled from her home state down to Arizona to show off Bill's new baby. Even though Skee and baby Kathy had stayed with Irene, Jim's mother wrote as though Skee just handed the baby over to Irene to care for. If true, Jim hadn't heard any complaints from his wife about it. He took a moment to picture Irene with a baby in her arms and smiled at the mental image. However, his smile faded just a bit to recall that, in a couple of recent letters, a few pointed remarks from his young wife made it clear that she very much desired a home of her own. When he returned from the war, she wanted to find a place on the other side of town as far from his parents as possible.

He decided he would do his damndest to make that happen, even though it might take precious time to accomplish during a short leave home before shipping out again. The lines in Yuma marked themselves quite clearly — the relationship between his wife and his mother drew a strong parallel to the Siegfried Line, "Dragon's Teeth" and all.

Chapter Seventeen

Germany
April 17, 1945

My Dearest:

I had an interesting experience the other day. I was left in a German town to guard a bunch of German guns and half-tracks and ammunitions. My squad leader had been evacuated and I was put in charge of the squad. That left myself and 8 men to protect the equipment and take charge of a town full of Germans! We finally destroyed all the equipment except one German half-track and myself and another fellow drove it 60 miles to rejoin our company.

It's rather risky to be driving German equipment over here, but we made it O.K. and nobody hurt. Things like that make life more interesting over here and I'm getting to like chasing those Krauts. We sure have taken lots of prisoners lately.

Just heard the news that President Roosevelt is dead. That is something I hate to hear because it might lessen my chances of getting home as soon as this is over.

The food situation is pretty good and I am getting to be a chicken and egg thief. These civilians have a lot of eggs and we liberate some occasionally.

No more news for now that I am able to share. I miss you and hope to be seeing you soon.

All my love,
Jim

Strains of music and the sound of men singing softly to the mellow moan of a harmonica brought Jim out of a snooze. He climbed up out of his bedding to check on the men up and down the line. Once he saw all was well and calm, he moved back where a few soldiers from his squad gathered. When the tune ended, Jim commented, "That's a nice sound. I don't believe I ever heard that song, fellas. What is it?"

The harmonica player came from Jim's squad. Also named James, he hailed from Colorado. Looking up from his harmonica, he spoke up in answer to the question.

"It's called the *88 Blues*, James." To keep things straight in the field, the squad had decided to call the Colorado fellow *Jimmy*. And Colorado Jimmy called Jim by the more formal *James*, though the other guys in the squad continued to refer to him as *Jim*, as they were accustomed to do. It wouldn't work to risk a chance of mistaken identity with the kind of night work going on these days. Clean communication was hard enough and added confusion over which James/Jim/Jimmy you wanted could cost lives.

Colorado Jimmy added, "I wrote the song myself. It's about that blasted German artillery — you know the 88mm monster that keeps us up all night? I've been dreaming about that gun, and the song kind of wrote itself while I slept. I'm hoping that playing about it keeps it far away from me. The words go well with the tune if you'd like to join in."

These fellows had many monsters to keep at bay. One of the things that plagued Jim's dreams at night was the sight of their own squad leader, hit by the blow-back of debris from an exploded tank shell. He and a fellow from another unit had dragged him back out of harm's way and to the medics. They hoped he would receive the help he needed, but no word had yet come to reassure them.

Jim would never forget the look on the wounded soldier's face, the crimson blood painting the fear-leached pallor of his skin. In last night's dream, Jim had relived the entire experience in an eerie silence that intensified the sight of the blood, the cold clumsiness of feet and fingers as they tried to handle the body without doing damage, and the blazing burst of flame through darkness.

A shell-shocked moon feebly illuminated the path, attempting to guide their footsteps. He had jerked awake in terror, the soundlessness of the dream echoed in his wakefulness, the deafening effect of the blast giving way to dull humming in ears made sore by the explosion. It had been that close.

Sitting now in a bombed-out farmhouse, in yet another muddy field, joining his voice with the other soldiers to the tune played by the soldier from Colorado, Jim settled back into a warmer place. Soon, as the strains of the harmonica soothed them, word passed quickly from man to man that the mail truck had just rolled in.

Without any sight or sign of the enemy for a while, one man from each squad cautiously emerged from the scant protection of their bunkers, swiftly and silently, with movement orchestrated as though choreographed and well-rehearsed, to travel through the woods and collect the treasured mail delivery.

Jimmy pocketed his harmonica. "My mouth needs a break. I'll go play postman." He returned quickly with a banded stack of letters for the men and two rather large packages. The prized boxes caught the immediate interest of the entire squad.

"Who are the boxes for, Jimmy?" a voice called out, a little too loudly.

Jimmy joined the others in the make-shift shelter that they would call "home" for a few nights respite from the fighting. As each one found a place to stake out space for sleep, eventually two, and then three or more men, would join forces so as to share a common shelter. Those gathered with the sound of Jimmy's voice looked up expectantly, and a bit longingly, at the packages he held.

Jimmy lowered the volume of his voice to answer, "These are both addressed to one of the gentlemen among us named James. I sure wish one of them said Jim on it. I'd claim it myself. But then I would have to fight Hendrickson for them."

"Hand those over here, Colorado. Let's see what we've got." The first package Jim opened came from, of all places, Lockheed. "Look at this," he called out quietly, "a bunch of the folks I worked with at the plant in Burbank sent a care package after all this time. Do you suppose it took the Army this long to find me? I haven't been in Burbank for going on a year now." Jim examined the contents and started to chuckle. "Here, guys, you all can share this one and, sight unseen, I'll keep what's in the box from my wife." He handed the box to the soldier next to him who rustled through it, groaning as he discovered toothpaste, toilet paper, two tooth brushes and other toiletries.

"No wonder you're willing to give this away. They must not know that we get all this kind of thing from the Army. Not a morsel of food or even a deck of cards. Man, what I wouldn't give for a chocolate bar right now."

"I just appreciate that they took the trouble to send it. I won't tell them any different. I'm surprised they haven't forgotten all about me by now." Jim picked up the other box from Irene. "O.K., men, we hit pay dirt. Look what my Irene sent me." The tone of his voice drew the entire squad in close, hunkering down shoulder to shoulder in the meager protection of shaky walls and partial roofing.

One of the guys used his cigarette lighter to cast a glow on the contents of the open box. There, glistening in the gleam of the flame, like a pirate's treasure, glowed, not piles of gold, but stacks of *Oh Henry* and *Hershey* bars. The men stared in awe at the candy, and no one moved.

"Wow, I wonder how many ration cards she had to save up to send this over. Let's divide these up, men, and make them last, what do you say?"

Each man took just one of the coveted chocolate bars, handling it as though it might disappear the way a fragment of a dream fades with dawn.

"You know, Jim," Edgar spoke up, "if that wife of yours ever gets tired of you, I would be happy to take on your job. That's quite a gal you've got. I've seen her picture enough times, and she is mighty pretty, too. How come she linked up with a mug like you?"

"Just my luck, you know," said Jim. "I sent her flowers, not too long ago. She hasn't said a word about them, and I've asked her a couple of times in my letters. Either she never got them or my mother intercepted the delivery and kept them for herself.

"I hate saying it, but my mother would do something like that. Irene has hinted that she wants her own place when I get back. I'm going to make damn sure that happens, one way or another."

"You tell that little gal that every one of the members of G company think she is just swell. Mothers are like that, sometimes. They just can't seem to let their sons go, no matter how good a gal the new wife is," Jimmy from Colorado commented. "And I've yet to meet a woman worth her salt who wants to share a kitchen with her mother-in-law."

The welcome excitement of the care package died down, as each man returned to his own spot of shelter. A full moon cleared the cloud cover to shine down into the silence while some of the men reflected on their own memories of women back home. Jim and Edgar stayed together and unwrapped another *Hershey* bar to share, savoring the welcome warmth of chocolate melting as it dispelled the stale taste of countless cigarettes.

"You know, Edgar, this country sure is a strange one. I don't like most of the things I've seen over here, and though we have stumbled on some nice people, I believe that no mercy should be shown to the civilians. They have treated the captured laborers with a lot of unnecessary brutality. That one Polack boy we talked to claimed that when the Yanks occupied his village, the German he worked for started to feed him about five times as much as before they showed up. And that amount wasn't enough food either by my notion."

"I agree with you, Jim. We're in a pretty good place often enough these days, with the cows, fresh milk, eggs and all. But if we didn't have the military chow — and your wife's care packages — we would all pretty much starve. When you write her, tell her thanks for me, will you?"

"You bet I will." The two men gazed up at the now-lightening sky. "You know, just after we got married, Irene and I did some gazing at that old moon before we took off to check in to the Hotel San Carlos for the night. There's a place called Prison Hill that looks out over the Colorado River. They have a guard tower that looks out over the water; a Gatling gun still mounted there used to make outlaws from the territory think twice about trying to escape. Sounds like a strange place to take your new bride, I know, but the beauty of the place seems stronger because of the sorrow and sadness the place carried with its burden of history.

"It's like that over here, somehow. And right this minute, I could almost wish Irene was here with me to look at that moon in spite of the danger and ugliness here." The silence between them hung there for a while. "No offense, Edgar, but my wife is sure a lot prettier and smells a good deal better than you do too."

"Thanks a lot Hendrickson," and they started to laugh.

The two men sat in the pale light, holding on to their letters with both hands and peering intently at the pages. They would soon need to grab some sleep before the next day brought more challenges, made a bit more palatable with a distant memory of chocolate comfort from far away to sustain them.

Chapter Eighteen

April 23, 1945
Germany

Hello Butch:

Received 6 nice letters from you today and a couple from Virginia. You were asking about our uniforms. It consists of O.D.'s, field jacket, cartridge belt, and in my case I'm carrying a Browning automatic rifle which I wouldn't trade for anything in the weapons line. We never wear fatigues over here at all because they are the same color as a Jerry uniform and too many G.I.s would be shooting G.I.s.

Butch, I'm not in the least worried about our financial status. It's just that I like to know how you are making out. You are doing swell, but remember not to live too cheaply. We didn't before I left so there's no reason for you to deprive yourself of anything you need.

The weather here isn't very good now, but we are in houses so nobody's hurting. Back in the Ardennes was really some rough weather, as I guess I have often said. We would try to dig foxholes in the frozen ground through the snow, and water would seep in and freeze before we got a foot down through the soil.

One night I had to wade across a stream while we were attacking and for the next 24 hours I walked around with a bunch of ice in my shoes and my clothes frozen to above the knees. I certainly feel sorry for the boys who had to spend all winter in that stuff.

Friday the 13th was indeed a lucky day for me. We ran into a battery of Jerry rocket guns and 7 half tracks and took them over. That was at Stein horst and is where my squad caught up with the company driving one of them. We stayed there for 2 days and we were beginning to think trouble was brewing when we took off to catch up.

135

I have received the air mail stamps and thanks a lot. We are able to buy them now, so you won't have to send more. I could use some more candy if you should get a hold of some.

I also received the pictures of you, Ray, Kathy and Dad. Kathy seems to have her father, Bill's ears, and Pop has more white hair, which he should have with such a family to cope with. You still look beautiful as always and I sure wish I could be with you.

Have to close,

Jim

"Your name is Smith? Welcome. I'm your squad leader and you can call me Jim. Where have you been before you got here, Smith?"

Smith, with the dazed gaze of a man plucked out of a soft bed and thrown out into the cold, looked around the clearing with wary watchfulness, as though trying to spot a place to hide. Jim had seen that look before on the faces of soldiers brand new to the fighting. Lately, most of the men he worked with stared at the world through eyes schooled to mask pain, revealing only resigned acceptance and envisioning more dreary days ahead. He worried about those men.

"I was attached to headquarters, Jim. I must have pissed somebody off because all of a sudden, I'm in the middle of a forest that seems to have guns blooming from the tree limbs. But don't worry about me; this can't be too rough compared to the horrible places I've bedded down in lately."

Jim figured that Smith was in for a big surprise if they hit more trouble. The difference between moving around through mud as part of the HQ operation, then ducking under screaming Meemies and 88mm artillery, kind of compared to the difference between sitting in the bad-boy corner of Mom's kitchen and doing hard time for a felony.

"I'll tell you, Smith, we are looking to come closer to the Russians any time now. I sure would like to see old Joe Stalin coming over the skyline. Their armies have been rolling along according to the reports we've heard. They're making our job just that much easier by doing that, too, because the Jerries don't know which way to jump. But we have to stay on our toes. You'll be fine."

"How long have you been in action, Jim?"

Jim understood that Smith was trying to figure out who mattered in this part of the world. He would soon learn that the line between headquarters and the field gapped over a pretty wide distance most of the time.

"I've been leading this squad since our staff sergeant was evacuated. I think the Army may have forgotten that there is a PFC running the show for his unit down here. But it won't much matter if you are a private or a captain when the trouble starts. Bullets don't salute. You just stay close to us and help watch our backs. We'll be watching yours."

Jim appreciated these few days of quiet bunking on an abandoned farm between nights in rough camps during battle conditions. He took quite a ribbing the first time he sat down next to a cow and started milking. But it wasn't long before he got his men settled to squatting positions on the ground, each snuggled up next to a German cow, working the udders like champs, and streaming fresh milk into whatever containers they could liberate.

He finally sent a couple of guys to the barn where they should have taken the cows to begin with. Stools made the job much more efficient, and available buckets were put to good use quickly. As he and the boys played "farmer" for a while, Jim rested his head against the cow's warm belly and planned his next letter to Irene while his pail foamed with fresh milk.

It would be five months since he had left Irene in Burbank and ten months since his training had begun. That time weighed on him like years, not months. He wanted to tell Irene about Sergeant Taylor, the guy from Denver who shared his first name. This other James and his wife shared a wedding anniversary date with Jim and Irene too.

Colorado Jimmy had just gotten a battlefield commission as a Second Lieutenant, and the guys had all ribbed him because that made him a commissioned service man serving in a squad led by a PFC.

Jim figured they would lose Colorado Jimmy to a transfer that should come with his rise in rank. He hated to see that. He had come to look at Jimmy as one of the men he wanted at his back, someone to have with you in a fight because you knew he would stick close. He felt that way about Edgar, too, the soldier who had been with him the longest of any of the men over here.

He also worried about his wife. It was almost May, and she had two more months to go before the baby came. She had gone through her entire pregnancy without him and while the news accounts seemed optimistic that the war would soon end, Jim still had seen a lot more danger in fighting than he had shared with her. He wondered if the newspapers got the same kind of reports from the fighting that he gave to Irene.

He hoped he wasn't the only one trying to paint a rosier picture for the folks back home. Some of the things they found as they traveled deeper and deeper into the heart of German power chilled him to the stomach and froze his guts.

He wanted to go home to Irene. But first, he needed to see Bill walk out of one of those prison camps. He prayed each night that Bill had landed where there were decent folks running things in a humane way. Wouldn't it be great if his brother Bill had a cow to provide him fresh milk like his own squad had today?

Jim finished up with the cow, put her to grazing safely, and carried the milk in to cool. In the quiet, he would write quickly, having already penned the letter in his head. He wondered if the scent of cow would last to tease Irene's nose as she opened the envelope back in Yuma.

Chapter Nineteen

May 2, 1945
Germany

My Dearest:

Received another letter from my Honey today in which you said you hadn't received a letter in some time. There were a couple of letters I wrote in April that I lost as there was no mail service working for a while. We were moving very fast and I was kind of lucky to write what little I did get to send.

I was gone when the man came around for money orders again. He came by once and only about half of the group were able to get them. When and if ever I catch him I can send quite a bit. We had a good old Army dice game last night and I came out $10.00 to the good.

Honey, when Junior puts in an appearance, if I'm not around, will you have a duplicate made of the birth certificate and send it as soon as possible? I have to take it to headquarters for you to get the additional allotment. Here's hoping yours truly is out of the Army by that time.

If our commanding General does volunteer the Division for Army of Occupation or to fight the Japs, I think I'll have a furlough and should make it.

There is a report that Adolph is "Kaput" (dead), and I am hoping that is true. If you see Ray, tell him he had better stay out of the Army as he will be sure to get an occupational job of guard duty. Even though the war seems to be winding down, there is still danger in the aftermath of the big fighting.

The old farmer whose land we are living off of just came back and wants a chat, so I'd better go and indulge him.

All my love,
Jim

The old man watched carefully as Jim finished signing his letter. Hands clasped behind his back, he rocked back and forth a bit, as though about to burst forth with something he held inside, eager to share. Jim held up one finger to indicate he would be a minute longer, and then remembered that the German farmer could speak English a whole lot better than he could speak German.

"Just a minute, please, Herr Heinrich. I want to pack these letters away carefully so they don't get lost before the mail truck shows up this time. My wife worries when she doesn't hear from me regular."

Heinrich smiled and unclasped his hands, nodding his willingness to wait. Jim carefully sealed the envelope, stamped it and wrote the address: *Mrs. Irene Hendrickson P.O. Box 114 Yuma, Arizona.* He added this last one to three others written while staying at Heinrich's farm. He hoped the mail trucks would soon catch up with the men staying here. He knew he wasn't the only one of the soldiers who hungered for home contact after their weeks of heavy fighting. Mail received during down time was even more welcome after battle action. Jim always felt like a letter from home brought back his sanity.

With his letters wrapped safely in oil cloth, Jim turned his attention to the farmer, remembering their late night dice game. The night before, his squad had gathered around a fire and someone pulled out the dice. The sound of their laughter and jollying each other around had attracted the German farmer's notice. The men weren't sleeping in his farm house, not much was left of it after the bombings. No one knew whose bombs had blasted away the walls, leaving just a rock hearth, chimney, and part of the living room.

Heinrich still took shelter there though, and the men bunked quite comfortably in an extra barn at the back of the house.

Heinrich had already rebuilt his main barn and chicken coops and begun to work on the main house. As far as Jim had seen, there was no family or fellow German to help him with the work.

Jim had noticed Heinrich last night, sitting off in the distance, just watching the men, focused on the dice game as intensely as they had been on dinner after a day without food. He had stood up and hollered, "Hey, Herr Heinrich, how would you like to join a bunch of American G.I.s so we can show you how to lose some of those Reich marks?"

Smith, the newest member of the squad, the transfer from HQ duty, had looked up in surprise. "I thought we had a policy of non-fraternization with the enemy. You want to play dice with a Kraut?"

The circle quieted immediately. Jim looked at the men around him and gauged the expressions on their faces.

"Here's the deal, Smith. We are in this man's country, billeted on his property, eating his eggs and fresh vegetables that he grew on his soil and drinking milk from his cows. Like it or not, he sent three sons to Hitler's war, and they aren't coming home. Herr Heinrich over there has treated us just fine since we got here three days ago. I know about that non-fraternization order, but if we can't just be men together with the locals, then I don't know why we fought this war in the first place. Tell you what, if any man doesn't want to throw the dice with our German host, he is excused to go hit the sack. What do you say?"

Smith smiled a bit sheepishly. "That's just fine with me, Jim. I don't see any problem taking his money if you don't."

Jim relaxed and nodded one more time before he walked over to Heinrich who sat unmoving during the fuss. He wasn't sure how much of the discussion the man had understood, but he knew it would take more than a hollered invitation to get him to join the group now.

"How about it, Heinrich? Do you know how to play craps?" Heinrich looked puzzled. "Dice, you know how to gamble? To bet?"

"Hah! I do!" Heinrich grinned from ear to ear. "One minute..." The old man headed off to what was left of his farm house and Jim lost sight of him in the shadows. He watched for a bit and then returned to the light of the fire.

"I think he is coming, but I can't be sure he understood us. If he joins us, we might have to teach him the game."

The German farmer stumbled back to the firelight, his gait weighed down by his heavy burden. A huge corked jug crooked under his arm challenged his strength as he lugged it over.

"Is that what I think it is?" Jim asked, wondering what he had gotten them in for.

"*Gut schnapps*," Heinrich chortled. "No gambling without the good drink to make the dice roll right."

"Well, Smith," Jim had chuckled, "I guess this German fellow knows what it takes to play dice after all."

The German's moonshine liquor might have received a warmer welcome than the German did from some of the men, but the addition of these unexpected alcoholic spirits went a long way to lift their emotional spirits. The dice game outlasted the contents of Heinrich's jug and they played until late under the stars.

So this early morning after a late night at dice, Jim felt surprised to see Heinrich up and spry as fresh grass. Jim finished putting his letter away and turned to him. The old fellow looked about to explode with whatever it was he wanted to share.

"What can I do for you this morning, Heinrich? You aren't going to try to get me to give you your money back from last night's game, are you?"

"Hah! No. You keep my German money. It's probably worth nothing now anyway."

They both chuckled at that a bit and the old farmer continued, "I have two things. One, I hear that Hitler is *kaput*. He should rot in hell. I hope it is true, that report."

"I had heard that, too, Heinrich. But so far it is just rumor. We have an American expression, *wishful thinking*. But I wouldn't waste too many tears on a dead *Führer* either."

Heinrich laughed loud at that. "*Der Führer*! Ha. How did you know? That is my second thing to talk with you about today. I need your men to help me slaughter *Der Führer* for tonight. Then we have a party."

"Say what?" Jim couldn't believe what he had heard. This old farmer thought his unit could go after Hitler and execute him? Was he crazy after all? "Have you been drinking more jugs of whiskey, Herr Heinrich? What are you talking about?"

Heinrich motioned Jim to follow, chuckling and mumbling in German that Jim couldn't catch a word of. He moved along after the old geezer, but moved warily, shifting gears to battle alertness. The pen beyond the barn nestled in the shade of trees that looked as though they had flourished for hundreds of years. In the pen, several young steers, fat and sleek from the rich bounty of the land, thrived with the careful tending of the old farmer.

"Here," hollered Heinrich, "see that one in the middle? The white one with the black mark under the nose? That, Jim, is *Der Führer*. If you and your men help me to butcher, we will eat veal steak for dinner tonight. It is time for *Der Führer* to do some good in this world, yes?"

Heinrich had said the magic word as far as Jim was concerned. If the old farmer wanted to feed them a steak dinner, that would be fine with him. And so he left Heinrich to tend their prize captive. He would rouse the men and give them the news. *Der Führer's* days would end that night on the grill. He hoped they would indeed see the last of the German *Führer* as well. But for tonight, a belly full of beef would be most welcome. Alive or dead, Hitler was not invited to this feast.

Chapter Twenty

May 6, 1945
Germany

My Dearest:

Received your letter of April 27, with the 4 pictures. The pictures are very good and you look as if you had a good tan. From your letters, it sounds as if Junior has quite a wardrobe now.

As you now know, we have met the Russians. They are a happy-go-lucky bunch of guys and the stuff they drink—WOW. It is the original white lightning and puts the old Kentucky moonshine at the foot of the class.

Everything is clearing up over here. Seems to me like it's taking a long time though. We have moved again and it has been three days since I've had a chance to mail letters. We are pulling some pretty rough guard duty now. Guess I'll set up a guard roster when I get home. I will be so used to doing it by then.

No news I can tell you, except I love you, and that's not news.

All my love,

Jim

And thanks again for the pictures.

11:45 P.M.

My Dearest:

Tonight we heard, (via rumor grapevine), that the war was over. Whether that is true or not, I don't know. I do know that we have cleaned up our sector and our objective is accomplished. There will be a lot of mopping up and patrolling to do for a while so you can see that I'm not as pleased as I thought I'd be to hear the news. It only means that my life is safer now, but that hasn't worried me since my first day of combat.

In my opinion, the war is over when I get that discharge and return home to you. Am hoping I don't draw Army of Occupation, even if it means I'll have to fight the Japs. Just so I get to see you before I go to the Pacific.

We have been having a hell of a time with the POWs. Too damned many to handle and it has worked all of us a lot. The only celebration we have had so far was a good dice game and that cost me about $50.00. Someday I'll learn, maybe.

In the last fighting, I managed to get another P-38 pistol which I hope to be able to hang on to as a souvenir. You remember someone 'liberated' the last one I found from my Jeep.

My squad leader is still in the hospital and I've still got the squad to take care of. Boy I wish he would get back 'cause I've been running this outfit for three months now, and it is a lot of responsibility for a PFC. It's past bedtime, Honey. I must get up early, so I'll close for now.

All my love,

Jim

May 8, 1945
Germany

My Dearest Irene:

Received your letter of April 28 a while ago. It must be hotter than hell in Yuma now. Sure do hope it isn't too much for you to stand.

I just returned from an interesting experience. Last night after supper, they called me over to Company headquarters where they gave me some clean clothes and told me to park myself there for the night. This morning, they drove me up to Regimental Headquarter and the Colonel from Regiment pinned the Silver Star medal on me. Am sending the medal and citation to you as soon as I make connection with our elusive mail clerk.

Remember when I wrote you that Friday, April 13th had been a lucky day for me? It was for action on that day that they gave me the medal. There wasn't much to it really, although they sure made it sound good on paper.

The war is now officially ended and we are going to be Army of Occupation until we get reorganized anyway. There are lots of rumors going around now, but nobody knows the score on anything just yet. Am hoping to go fight the Japs because that will mean I get a 45 day furlough with you and Junior. Wish I could be there now to celebrate the war's end, etc.

You wrote that your Aunt Phon wanted you to go to Colorado before Junior gets here. I don't think that is advisable for you to take the trip now, Honey. If you could go in a car it would not be so bad, but those darned trains are rough enough in normal times to ride that far on. Am still pulling all the strings I can on this end to get home by June 23d.

3:30 P.M.

Just got back from a good hot shower. The first I've had since March 27. I took a couple of sponge baths, but there's still nothing like a good hot shower. That was almost better than the medal.

When I returned, there was another letter from you dated April 20. Also one from Mom. Have not written to her for some time, so had better close for now.

All my love,
Jim

Jim quickly reread the ending of his letter as he folded the thin onion-skin paper. He winced at the closing comment, realizing that Irene would not appreciate knowing that he was signing off quickly with her to write to his mother. He hoped she would note the time and forgive him for the slight. He loved his mother, but the obligation of writing to her could not compare with the lifeline to sanity that came from writing to his wife. He made a mental note to thank her for that lifeline in his next letter.

He looked around his accommodations for the night, a small room with two beds intended for double occupancy, but he had the room all to himself. A real bed, pillow and blankets! What luxury. He considered sleeping in both of them, but settled on the one nearest the window. The view looked pretty dreary, but at least he didn't have to look at cows, mud, or machine guns. It had taken him a while to discover the common shower and bathroom, a short walk down a clean, but colorless hallway.

A few other men, there like he was to receive their own commendations from battle, shared the dormitory. He figured that these nice and home-like rooms belonged to the officers assigned to regular duty at this facility. He felt privileged to share their soft sheets, if only briefly.

The Silver Star medal sat right next to the bed on the small night table with a lamp and clock. He thought he might read the citation one more time, and then decided he was just too tired to do anything but sleep. He might as well enjoy the bed while he had it. The next morning he would leave this oasis of peace and clean comfort for the grimy reality of scrabbling in a field with the other soldiers.

He pulled the clean cotton sheets and soft blanket up over his shoulders, and nested his head in the pillow, appreciating luxuries that he used to take for granted back home. When he closed his eyes, his mind projected a dim replay of the action of April 13th spooling in his head like a cinema reel.

If Irene knew what he had risked to stand up and lead a charge like that, she would probably do what the Germans had failed to accomplish and wring his neck. The other soldiers in the field that day had analyzed a situation they considered too dangerous. Smart enough not to pretend they could dodge the bullets that strafed the ground, trees, and sky all around and above them, they had hunkered down in what small illusion of safety they could manage.

Jim didn't think he had done anything that heroic; he just got disgusted with laying low, waiting for a bullet to find him in the shallow dirt shelter. His captain had urged them forward, calling from behind them to charge. To a man, they had decided to ignore his pleas. Captain Felton hadn't sounded too convincing anyway.

So Jim had jumped up and hollered, "Hell, if no one else will go, then I will." The others, probably as sick of the tense waiting as he was, had fallen in with him and done the job.

They took out the machine gunners first and then eliminated the ones who refused to come as prisoners. Their training, all those endless games of "cops and robbers," served them well.

If they really wanted to reward heroics, they had missed the mark. By Jim's way of thinking, what he had done for that medal was probably one of the stupidest moves he had ever made. It just took someone with the gumption — or the stupidity — to go first. Jim figured his gumption came from being disgusted and impatient with the situation. He considered himself, and the other men, damn lucky to have survived it.

He recalled another incident, though, not long before that headlong charge that took the hill, when no one had taken any special note. That time, in his mind, took more courage. One night on guard duty, he had traveled the line, looking in the foxholes to make sure all the men were settled in safely.

He didn't know these men well. Other squads had been attached recently for a united push, and the line stretched long beyond his own squad. He came upon a hole dug a distance from the others. It looked a bit strange to him for some reason, not trenched exactly like an American G.I. would have set it up, so he took a careful look at the man dozing down in it.

They had heard the stories of Nazi soldiers who robbed Americans of their uniforms — even stealing them from the dead on the field when the opportunity arose. This fellow had on an American sergeant's field jacket, but the rest of the uniform did not match up. Then Jim saw the fellow open one eye — he had only pretended to sleep. Jim saw red. He reached down into that hole in the dirt and dragged the fellow up by the scruff of his neck. Calling softly down to the next fox hole, he rounded up some help and they took the man prisoner. As they restrained the German, something heavy dropped into the dirt. It was a P-38 pistol, cocked and ready to shoot. Jim looked at the members of his squad and steadied his voice at the sight of their dropped jaws.

"Well," he said, "I guess this souvenir belongs to me." He picked up the gun, emptied the chambers of the bullets that might have provided him, or one of his men, a last meal of lead in the belly. He pocketed the weapon. "We won't report this to the brass."

The men nodded grimly, shaken to silence at the thought of what might have become a much different ending to the excitement. They then had herded their prisoner off to add to other Germans who had become their responsibility over the last few days in the field.

Tonight, after receiving the Silver Star and commendation, barely awake as a fog of sleep slowly began to close around him in the dormitory at headquarters, Jim glimpsed the scene once more, and saw — instead of the face of the German Nazi — his brother Bill. He jolted wide awake, breathing hard with a heartbeat like artillery fire. Where had that come from? Then finally, again calming himself down with thoughts of home and the softness of his temporary quarters, he fell deeply asleep and slept the night through, more peacefully than he had for the last five months.

Chapter Twenty-one

May 10, 1945
Germany
9:30 P.M.

Hello Butch:

Just received another letter from you and find that the thermometer is heating up in Yuma as usual. It is still on the coolish side over here with quite a bit of rain that raises hell with a guy when he is on guard duty.

Reminds me, I must go out on guard duty in a little while now. War or no war, the Army still believes in lots of Guard Duty, which as you know by my letters, irks me no end.

Don't worry about the car, Honey. I'll take care of that when I return. All you worry about is taking good care of you and Junior until I get there. Then you can start taking care of me too.

We were measured for Eisenhower jackets tonight. Also took our cap sizes. I don't know just what's cooking yet.

Must cut this short and go patrolling. They expect a guy to be punctual as hell—Bah!

All my love, as always, Jim

P.S. Nasturtium is your spelling lesson for today.

"Well howdy! I guess we told Adolph a tale or two. Wake up, you men, the war is over!"

Jim opened one eye to squint up at the loud voice of his Sergeant who had finally returned to service the day before. The fella looked well-fed and robust, like he'd enjoyed a good long vacation in a resort or something, instead of confinement to an Army field hospital.

"Hell, Sarge," Jim mumbled, "war or no war, the news could wait until a fellow finishes his shut-eye. I barely got two hours of down time last night with patrol duty — and these other soldiers could use a bit of sack time too."

A groaning chorus of assent from the squad added a counterpoint of harmony to Jim's sentiment.

"Ya'll can sleep later on, we have an assembly to make this morning before chow, so fall out of those bunks and make it snappy. I can't believe you aren't chomping at the bit to hear how they finally got old Hitler's goat. Now let's go."

The official news of the war's end should have been of great interest to these men. But they had been listening to rumors for weeks. It probably wouldn't make one bit of difference to them in their daily walk any time soon, even if the news turned out to be true this time.

The Army had a system for sending the troops home. A soldier's time slot to ship home to the states depended on a complicated allocation of points awarded for time in battle, number of dependants, etc. End of service in Europe would also depend on available transport across the ocean.

How well he remembered the long delay before an ocean liner finally showed up to ferry him across the Atlantic to get him here. He didn't think the return trip home would be any quicker.

The men scrambled to free themselves from their rough bedding and clean up the worst of the ravages from another night sleeping in an abandoned barn on beds of straw. As they roused themselves, the declaration of the end of the war in Europe did sober them a bit, giving cause for reflection and some consternation about past and future. They had walked many miles and lost as many good men along the way. Still, what lay ahead remained uncertain. The Army would make the decision about what came next for each one of them. Some would be assigned to the Army of Occupation, charged with the grim duty of traveling through towns bombed by both Nazi forces and Allied troops. Others would face the uncertainty and continued distance from home as they traveled to fight in the Pacific.

The future weeks or months would still be fraught with the tension of "mopping up" the last die-hards from the enemy's side, taking them as prisoners or eliminating them if they posed a threat to life. Slowly, the devastation of war and damage might recede, due to the combined efforts of the citizens who survived and joined the Occupation forces in efforts to rebuild. The Americans would stay for a while to organize a peaceful return of property and order.

Jim began to worry, again, about Bill. He had pretty much given up on the glorified vision that had brought him into this war. He now knew there would be no fantasy scenario where he would miraculously spring his brother from a German prisoner of war camp. With the end of the war a reality, Bill's time in prison would probably end for him too, as it had for so many other men in this place Jim had come to regard as a cesspit of a country.

He hoped to hear soon that William Clarence Hendrickson had arrived safe and sound back at Mom Hendrickson's front porch. He wanted to go home and find him eating peach cobbler and telling tall tales to the folks, no doubt playing a starring role in Hitler's defeat. His brother had always been one to land in the rose petals when, more often than not, he deserved to crash in the manure pile instead.

Jim smiled at the image of Bill on the top of a hill of ripe and fragrant *Bandini*. He sent mental good wishes to his brother, wherever Bill was. And then he let him go to face his own future. With a grin on his face that his squad leader mistakenly assumed came from pride in victory, Jim headed over to the assembly to hear what the Army had in store for him next.

Chapter Twenty-two

May 14, 1945
Germany

Dearest Irene:

Today still finds us many miles apart and me with no assurance that I'll be there in time for Junior to put in his appearance. Still the usual rumors, which more often than not, prove to be completely on the contrary to what we do. One says we will head straight for CBI and the next says we'll get discharged right away—just like Lockheed used to do. My only hope is that I will get home for a little while, but then I am ready for whatever they want us to do.

Am wondering how you have been feeling, how your folks are making out, and what you are doing before Junior arrives. I feel useless as hell sitting around doing very little work and getting lots of sleep, and too much time to think. I walk around this old Jerry house like an old Hound Dog with a sore tooth.

Have heard no news from Bill and it would really be a long chance that I would see him now for we are in a small town acting as a Military Government. He would have to come knocking on my door.

We are having no trouble with the civilians, but they are certainly a stupid bunch of people on the whole. They are scared to death that the Russians will come across the river after we move out.

Enclosed is a cartoon which was printed in the Division paper. Must close and get that rusty BAR of mine ready for the inspections which are due any time.

All my love,
Jim

"Make yourself useful and add another log to that fire, Jim. We'll head out as soon as we finish shining up these shoes and then work up a sweat adding to the wood box."

Jim carefully placed his most recent letter in his kit. "Sure wish we could find out where we go next, Sarge. Any word from the powers above or below?"

"Nary a sign, Jim. You know I would share with you, but I don't have the ear of the brass. Our orders don't seem to be preparing us for anything in particular. Some of the men will go home, I'm certain. Some of us will head straight to the China/Burma/India Theater. But that all depends on the allotment points and the availability of transport back to the states."

Jim sighed with soul-deep frustration. He wished they would hurry up and make things clear so he could decide which way he wanted to go. If it meant joining up to extend his tour of duty in the Pacific, he would do that in order to get a leave home before they shipped him out. Irene was due in July and he wanted, more than anything, to be with her when Junior came into the world. Having a child would add to his discharge credit, too, and shorten his service obligation time.

"I should be enjoying the break from work, but without goals and directives, the time seems to crawl by. It gives a man too much leisure time to think, and I don't believe that is healthy for a soldier, do you Sarge?"

"Well, Hendrickson, it's a sure thing they didn't send us over here to do any thinking. And some of the things we've been asked to do don't bear thinking about."

The sergeant crossed the room and stooped down in front of the fire, watching the flames from the fresh wood burst forward racing to see how fast they could send sparks up the chimney. The heat reached out and embraced the men with welcome warmth.

Jim shivered a bit at the sudden warm air against the cold. "I heard that the censorship rules have been lifted. Is that true, or just another rumor from someone saying what he wishes out loud?"

"We'll get the formal word in general orders, but yes, it's true. The relaxed rules on what you can write should make your letters home a bit easier. I've been thinking you should be the company scribe or something with all the mail you send off."

"Well, Sarge, it keeps me sane, to tell the truth. But my last few letters have tested my ability to come up with anything to talk about. Not much to say. But if the ban is lifted, I could go back and tell Rene where we've been and what we have seen since I got on the Queen Mary back in New York. Now that was a sight to see, for sure."

"Better you than me, Jim. I don't have a wife to write to, but if I did, I'm not sure I would know what to say to her at all. Most of the boys feel the same way. I still try to keep in touch with the folks back home though, if only to tell them how much I miss them."

"I write to stay sane. Writing letters to Irene keeps me from going crazy. Her letters back take me into the world where she is living, and I can see my home town through her eyes. I keep that picture in my mind, just like the ones in my wallet. It's like a life-line that will get me back there in one piece. And that, I am determined to do."

"Let's scare up the other men and see if we can't cut down a few German trees to feed this fire. We can at least keep the American G.I.s from freezing. Damn it all to hell and back, it sure got cold all of a sudden. Two steps away from the fire, and it's colder than blue blazes again."

The two men hollered up the rest of the squad and headed out into the forested land beyond the clearing. No fence was necessary to divide the farm land from the forest, as the trees surrounding the fields, buildings, and animal pens marked the boundary with strict precision as though cut with measured care. A drill sergeant couldn't have asked for straighter ranks.

The Americans took a certain perverse pleasure in chopping down a tree or two, purposefully disrupting the compulsive perfection of a rigid forest boundary created by some German farmer. Before long, their efforts warmed them from the unseasonal cold, and they stacked the wood high in piles tall enough to last them through the long, cold nights ahead.

III: The Occupation

Chapter Twenty-three

May 19, 1945
Germany (Bad Münder)

My Dearest Butch:

Am a little nearer to you now. We have moved from Wittenberg to the town of Bad Münder and are still doing a little Guard Duty and patrol work. The rumor is pretty strong that we are U.S.A. bound. However, it may take quite some time for them to arrange boats and train transportation for us. They have a lot of troops to get out of here, Honey, and personal priorities don't count. As long as I keep heading in the right direction, I won't complain too much.

They have relaxed censorship regulations now so I believe I'll give a brief account of where I've been and what I've done since I left the states.

About four o'clock on Christmas Eve we left Camp Ft. George Meade via train for the P.O.E. at Camp Shanks, N.Y. There were quite a few guys who didn't care for leaving on Christmas and went AWOL from there.

On New Year's Eve we were aboard the Queen Mary, listening to the people celebrate the coming New Year. About daybreak Jan 1, we pulled out for the open seas. Everybody began to realize that it would be a long time before we saw the U.S. again, and the Queen Mary was a quiet ship for the next couple of days. Nothing of any importance happened on the trip across and we reached Glasgow, Scotland on Jan 7.

We unloaded from the ship and immediately took a train to South Hampton in the southern part of England. That was a fast ride so you can see that we didn't get much of a chance to see England.

Jan 9 we got on an L.C.T. boat and took off for Le Havre, France. That place was a total wreck from the bombings and artillery fire. We got off the boat again and walked through Le Havre to some tents on the other side of town.

Le Havre was covered with about 2 ft. of snow and it was cold and wet. We were supposed to stop in Oxford, England for 2 weeks, but the reason they gave us for sending us on through was that we had suddenly received AAA priority to the front lines.

We were then loaded on the 40 and 8 boxcars and headed through France on the double. Jan 12, we got off the train at Neerwinden, Belgium where we zeroed in our rifles and froze a little more. From there we got on trucks and rode about 40 miles a day until I joined the Company. I was a tired and disgusted boy by the time I reached the Company as you could probably tell by my letters.

I reached G Company at a bad time, for they had just come back from a rough time up front and had lost quite a few men. I joined the 3rd Platoon and we stayed there for a couple of days.

My first attack with the outfit was a rough one. We were taken in trucks to about 6 miles this side of Behr, Belgium. We cleaned the Jerries out of 6 miles of woods on that first day and as soon as it got dark, we dug in and started ducking the 88's and mortar fire. I will never forget that cold snow and ice that night. I damn near froze to death.

We finally accomplished our mission and were pulled back for a rest not far from Lieze, Belgium. We stayed there and rested up for about 14 days and were taken to Gilhave, Holland for two days, and then we were put on the Siegfried Line near Worm—along the Roer River.

Must close this now Sugar and go patrol the road for awhile. Am hoping to see you soon, so keep taking good care of yourself for me.

All my love,

Jim

PS This will be a continued story and there is a lot I'm leaving out. I just wanted you to know where I've been in this world. You can get a map and will have an idea of where I've been.

"Your dad always was a great worrier," my mother tells me. "He said he understood that I didn't want him to stew, but he wanted the truth, nothing else. It was about then that he suggested that I move in with his mom and dad. Our letters came back and forth more slowly during this time. It was funny how his letter suggesting I move arrived when I was packing up the house. I was already moving! We tuned in to each other pretty well that way.

"I read those letters several times, and I got my maps out and push-pinned the names he mentioned, plotting his course. Puzzling out the German and Belgian towns took some doing with his handwriting. I took thread and connected the pins.

"I strung a long blue strand from the route I guessed at from Camp Roberts, and then across the ocean, as he left the states. Each time another place got named in the letter or reported in a news reel, I added a pin and blue-threaded his route. Kind of a game, I suppose. I hoped to use red thread to wind his route back home once he began to head that way. I hoped it would bring him home to me."

I love this image of my mother, like a real-life version of Dickens' Madame Defarge, using thread to stitch out a talisman of protection for the fighting man she loved. My mother embroidered a safe passage home my father. with cotton thread stretched on pins along the route she hoped my father would follow, guiding him along his path home to her once more.

May 28, 1945
Bad Münder, Germany

My Dearest:

Received two more letters from you this morning and you wrote that you have about $3,000 in bonds. I don't see how you are managing to save money on what you are getting, but you sure seem to be doing all right. I am going to have to let you handle the money when I return because you are doing better than I ever did!

I'm taking up the story again. I believe I quit on the Roer River. We were there holding the line for about 26 days. Nothing of any importance happened there except we had a few Buzz bombs come in and there was a lot of artillery. I don't remember the exact date we attacked across the Roer River, but we went from Boekend to Krefeld in about a week and a half. Dülken was our biggest battle and we lost quite a few boys.

I was separated from our company in Dülken and got a sniper and 3 prisoners before I rejoined them. Right after that, I remember I got one for Bill's birthday. It was a hell of a present, but the Kraut had a Burp gun and had shot two of our boys. About that time I was really thankful for my BAR. It has saved my life a number of times since then.

We stayed in Krefeld for a couple of days and moved to a little town called Rumeln. Our outfit reorganized there before we made the next attack.

On one of the last days of March, we jumped off across the Rhine River and headed in the general direction of Hanover. We were riding trucks on that deal and didn't have a bad time of it except for snipers. On April 10, we had taken Hanover.

The night after we took Hanover we pulled back to a little village and were strafed and bombed by a Jerry plane. Lt. Kloe and myself borrowed a jeep with a machine gun mounted on it and took off from the buildings to get the dammed Jerry, but we hadn't been shooting half a minute when he let go with another bomb.

It hit 50 feet from the Jeep and knocked the hell out of us, but neither he nor I were hurt other than being banged up a bit. That bomb caused 7 casualties in the Company, which was 500 yds. away. By this time I was sure that I still had my aces and would keep them.

The next day we pulled out again and on April 13th we hit the "screaming meemies" and halftracks at Stein horst. There is where I received that Silver Star.

My Squad of 7 men held the Jerry equipment and our Company didn't hit any bad resistance till we got to the Elbe where I rejoined the Company in the halftrack. We stayed at the Elbe for some time, collected about 10,000 prisoners, and here I am waiting to get back where I belong.

Will close the baloney and say I love you, which definitely is not baloney and you can believe that.

Always,

Jim

June 1, 1945
Bad Münder

My Dearest:

It is 10:45 and I just woke up from a two hour nap, which was topped off by one of the damndest nightmares I ever had. I very seldom dream, but this one was very vivid. It seemed that you were mad at me because you thought I was stepping out with another blonde and yours truly was having one hell of a time convincing you that I was innocent. I woke up before the dream was finished, so I don't know the happy ending to it. Perhaps I shouldn't eat so much for supper.

Your last letter reached me in six days. Not bad for Uncle Sam's mail service. Sure hope you are getting some good service on your end. Perhaps you recognize this paper. Mom sent it to me and, as I had written her already today, I decided to use it to write to you.

The orchestra of Glenn Miller is playing "Sunrise Serenade" on the BBC network and it sure reminds me of our apartment and the radio playing all the time. My thoughts continue to take me back to what you used to do and say. I remember the little things most of all. The way you used to fix your hair and worry about your clothes, the way you used to look in a house dress doing dishes, the way you used to pester me by coming and sitting on my lap when I was reading the paper, how we always managed to burn the toast at breakfast.

I will always be grateful to you for the wonderful time we had, although I probably didn't appreciate you as much as you would have liked. I'm a lucky guy, Butch, to have you for a wife, and I'm fully aware of it. Sure didn't know I was capable of missing anybody as much as I have missed you. When I first met you, I thought I was too conceited to fall for anybody as I fell for you.

This month will be one which we will always remember. Am with you all the way, Sugar. Must close for now.

I love you,
Jim

"Your dad had no way of knowing that, while he was writing his letter, his *Butch* had begun to deliver so early. We expected Junior to show up in mid-July. My sister, Rose, drove me to the hospital when we realized that my nagging backache had become contractions.

"Before long, I produced a beautiful baby, your brother, Jimmy. The nurse began the process of cleaning and swaddling him while he howled to raise the roof top. I remember thinking that his father would be able to hear that baby all the way over in Germany. I remember smiling for the first time in quite a while at the thought.

"As the nurse started to hand the small bundle to me, another pain made me yelp and that brought the doctor back to see what the fuss was about. The contractions continued, and all of a sudden, Dr. Phillips roared, 'My God, Irene, there's another one in there.' Then the blonde girl from your dad's letter joined us.

"I don't remember anything else about the birth itself. I suspect that the medical staff gave me some kind of gas to put me to sleep. The next thing I knew, I had two babies in hospital bassinettes side by side. The blonde girl, your sister Ginger, came home first when I was released. But Jimmy, the *Junior* your father so longed for, needed to stay a while as he required some feeding up."

My mother does not shy away from telling me that she was feeling angry with her absent husband during the delivery. She was even madder at the Army for keeping him so long. I ask her about the eerie quality of coincidence in my father's dream.

"I always thought that we had some kind of special connection that crossed the miles between us. Somehow, he just knew. I didn't get to read that letter for at least two weeks, and I sure needed to hear his loving words. I've always known how lucky I am to have married Jim Hendrickson."

Chapter Twenty-four

June 5, 1945
Germany

My Dearest:

We have moved again about 70 miles north of Frankfurt, in a town I believe is Weinheim. We have a pretty nice house to stay in and even have running water in the place.

The trip down was a long, tiresome ride on which I was able to see a lot more of Germany. Berlin and Hamburg are the only two large towns that I haven't seen in Germany and I know that they are just a replica of the rest. Nice towns turned into huge piles of brick and plaster.

This morning I got myself busy and washed all my clothes. They sure were dirty. How about coming over and ironing the damned things for me? I should be an expert by the time I reach home. (I'll bet I forget how pretty fast when I get home though).

Allowing 15 days for this letter to reach you, Junior might have put in his (or her) appearance by now. I know you are in for a lot of pain and misery, Honey, and would give anything to be there for moral support, if I couldn't do anything else.

When things get rough over here, I always feel better knowing that you are pulling for me, and hope it will be some consolation to you to know that I'm for you all the way.

I could sit by the hour and cuss the Army for not letting me be with you at this time—or am I just being sorry for myself?

Anyway, I love you and always will.

Your husband,

Jim

Heidelberg
June 6, 1945

My Dearest:

Here it is June 6 and one year from the time the boys landed on the Normandy beach. We have had a holiday today and stood retreat for the first time since I've been overseas. It seems silly as hell because we have no flag to salute and no bugler to sound off. Nevertheless, we go through the motions in the proper military manner.

Honey, the Captain told us that there would be another lull in the mail situation because of the fact that we moved so far so fast. I didn't finish a letter for a couple of days because we were on the darned trucks.

On the way here, General Eisenhower looked the outfit over. He was sitting in his car at the side of the road just out of Frankfurt. Since the smoke has cleared, I've seen a lot of Generals roaming around. Up till V-E Day, you would very seldom find even a Major on the front. That seems plausible because they can't do much planning on the front.

It has been 6 days since I received your last letter. Seems like a long time to yours truly. They're stressing this non-fraternization policy again. Sometimes the Army does some crazy things and that is one thing they really went haywire on.

There are a few in every bunch that will go hunt for a woman the first chance available, and no matter what the punishment they give out, they'll still do it. Am glad the female situation doesn't bother me. Have not seen any here yet that are worth looking twice at.

Perhaps I am prejudiced because of you, though. For me, there is only one gal, and that is you.

I love you as always,
Jim

"All cleaned up and ready for the next parade, right guys?"

Jim hoped the sergeant was just kidding, but it sure did seem like their outfit got the nod to appear every time the Army decided to stage a show-and-tell event for the big brass. It turned him on his head having to get all "gussied up" for parade duty. It was just plain make-believe compared to how they usually spent their days and nights.

"Tell me, Sarge, why do you think they picked us to do the honors for Commander Gilhen? I, for one, would rather have watched from the sidelines. No disrespect intended to the Corps Commander, of course."

"Well Jim," the sergeant looked around as he spoke, playing to the room of men listening to the exchange, "it must be because you are so handsome. What do you guys think?" He responded to the hoots and hollers in the room with a flourish towards Jim, who stood up and gave him a mock salute and a bow.

"You know that must be true, and I'm sorry I hadn't thought of that," Jim bantered back, keeping the laughter going. "That must be why General Eisenhower looked us all over so carefully from his Jeep as we headed here. Say, did anyone else spot him?"

Of course there wasn't a man in the company who hadn't noticed their commander looking over the troops. Dale Harms, a kind man with a commonsense way about him, piped up in agreement, "Sure, I saw him. And you can bet I stood a little taller and put a snap in my step too." Not the tallest soldier in the squad, Dale got a big laugh on that line, before the men dispersed and went on about their business for the day. Jim hung back a moment to continue his conversation with the sergeant.

172

"Seriously, Sarge, it's almost like they keep trotting us out for these special occasions because we represent some oddity or something of that sort. It seems like they just can't believe there are so many of us still around to salute them. And all of a sudden, there are brass hats wherever we go. Any idea what that is about?"

"I get your drift, Jim, and I think you have the right of it. No one really thought we would accomplish our objectives. I think the high hats just want to take a gander at us — to see what the survivors look like up close."

"My thoughts exactly. But when Eisenhower warned us that 'the eyes of the world would be upon us,' I didn't realize he meant it would be during parades. I guess I don't mind giving them a show," he added, "but I didn't expect that there would still be so much work to do before they send us back to where we belong."

Jim referred obliquely to the continued action of his unit. They spent their days and nights visiting German towns and villages, capturing prisoners, handling civilians, some who resisted them forcefully. Snipers still shot at the American troops from the safety of their hiding places in the forest or from abandoned buildings. While the threat of bodily harm decreased markedly, still every day dawned with new challenges and possible danger still in this period of declared victory.

It had come to be that a man took a slight risk going around a corner without getting his head shot off. Calling it "guard duty" made it sound innocent, but the grim reality contrasted greatly with the party atmosphere of parade drills and honors for commanders already heading home well before all the shooting had stopped. The "cleaning up" chores were left to the lesser ranks.

"I guess the regular guys going home first are the ones who were here from the beginning, so I don't grudge them safe passage back to the states. But I sure wish I had the points earned to go back home with them. These days I can't help but feel, more and more, that my wife should have me with her and that Uncle Sam could do without Jim Hendrickson."

With a nod to Jim of commiseration, the sergeant left their quarters and Jim followed him from the comfortable farm house that served as their current residence. The rest of the squad hadn't gone far, gathered in a circle smoking cigarettes, huddling in earnest conversation.

"What's the topic of the day, gentlemen?" the sergeant asked, concerned by the hushed tone of voices from the circle.

"We just heard about one of the men who got hauled over to the hoosegow," answered Edgar with a quick look at Jim. "Seems he got caught breaking the non-fraternization policy, enjoying much more than polite conversation with a German fräulein, you know?"

"We were warned that Eisenhower had stepped up enforcement of the policy," Jim said in sober pronouncement. "This might not be the whole picture, but I heard that the policy came down hard again because the Russians have turned some villages into their own brothels, taking women, girls and grandmas, willing or not, and violently too. We call that rape where I come from. Can't say I endorse that much."

Their sergeant spoke up, "Jim's got the right of it, men. Let's be clear on this issue. No one is going to get arrested for talking to the citizens, sharing a meal or a laugh. But if an American GI even looks like he is forcing himself on a gal, that won't go down well, I don't care who you are. And I also don't think it matters if you've gone two years without a soft hand on you either, that is not the way to act. That's not who we are."

Jim nodded and took out a fresh pack of cigarettes. He opened the cellophane from the bottom, tapped the paper box smartly on his palm, and offered them around the circle to the men. "I guess we all better stick with these smokes as a poor substitute for the girls we left behind."

When Jim got word that the mail truck was due he ran all the way to the drop station to beat the crowd. Now, with the truck long gone, he sat as though stunned, staring at the page in front of him. His thoughts had been focused even more than usual on Irene. A strange feeling of foreboding had churned in his stomach and made him feel short of breath with a panic that he seldom allowed himself to feel. He had been desperate to read her letters.

But then the clerk had handed him just a single telegram from his mother. Stunned, Jim thought the worst. His mother never would waste money on something like that unless the news was very important. He opened it with dread. Finally, he returned to camp without speaking to anyone, put pen to paper and began to write...

June 9, 1945
Heidelberg, Germany

My Dearest:
A couple of hours ago I received the news that it was twins after all our kidding about it. Congratulations, sweetheart. I only wish that I was there with you. In her telegram, Mom said you were all right, and am glad of that.

She also said that the twins were premature. Sure hope they are O.K. Mom didn't say whether it was 2 boys, 2 girls, or a boy and a girl, so I will sweat that out until I get the details.

You know, Honey, I can't think of a damned thing to say. Have been writing for 2 ½ hours on what little there is here so far. Guess I should wait until the shock wears off a little before I attempt this.

Cannot explain how I feel. I do feel a bit helpless being over here, but would just be a nuisance if I were around there. It is a good thing the bassinet is big enough for two, as you frequently mentioned.

The boys come around about every five minutes and kid me a little, but they are just jealous. Believe me, I'm proud of my wife and with good reason. Have not heard you gripe one single time since I've been over here and I know that you have had ample reason for a lot of griping.

Have read a few of the boys' letters over here and their wives have done a lot of griping. And I have done more than my share of it to you.

Will close for now, Butch.

I love you.

As Ever, Jim

Chapter Twenty-five

June 10, 1945,
Heidelberg or Mannheim (Darned if I know for sure where we are.)

One of the fellows turned over in his troubled sleep. Jim kept an eye on him. The kid who had found the wine the night before had gotten into a good bit of it before he decided to share it with the rest of the squad. Jim mentally cussed whatever German had hidden that cache of bottles so well that they had withstood, not only destruction from the blasting, but the looting afterwards. Somehow they had remained hidden in all the debris.

He looked at the boards, rocks and rubble that probably had once framed a pretty nice farm house, and shook his head at the devastation. He sure hoped there hadn't been anyone in that house when the artillery took it down.

When the fellows finally woke up, he thought it might be a good idea to find out which one of the enterprising soldiers had decided it was a good idea to check for a cellar. Their job was to find any civilians who were hiding or aiding German soldiers.

Quite a few of the Jerries had bailed out on their end of the war effort, taking refuge where they could find it in towns taken over by American soldiers. Some of them, though tired of fighting, refused to give up entirely. They hid in dark places like cornered skunks. The G.I. who found the wine needed a reminder to take more care about things like that. He could have found much more than wine in that dark and dangerous place.

The war might be officially over, but a fellow still needed to operate on full alert. So far Jim's squad had rounded up prisoners and evacuated unsafe buildings. And, so far, none had come to serious harm. Sometimes they blew up towns that had already been blown up once or twice by the Russians or by the Germans themselves.

But last night's bender had put them in some danger of their own making. Whatever soldier had checked the cellar had done the right thing — up to the moment he found all the wine and shared it with soldiers who soon weren't worth their salt for duty.

Taking stock this morning while the boys slept off the effects of the wine, Jim realized that his attachment to the 84th Infantry Division had sent him to be part of the 2nd Army, the 7th Army, the 9th Army, and now he was back with the 7th again. The boys from this group seemed like a good sort, and he was glad to be with them — until they had started to fight over who should take charge of the wine distribution.

To make it even worse, one of the fellows had taken a pistol and started shooting up a village in good old cowboy style before Jim and his sergeant could get to him. Wrestling a drunken shooter to the ground didn't rank too high on Jim's list for a good time. He could also bet money that there would be no battle medal given if he got shot for his efforts to save this soldier from himself. He didn't want to think about how close he and his sergeant had come to getting their heads blown off by one of their own men.

The gunfire and take-down had sobered the entire bunch of drunken sots, and, at about dawn that morning, they settled to sleep by this old wreck of a farmhouse. Jim and the sergeant scared up blankets, covered the men, and hoped they would sleep it off peacefully. They sure didn't need any more trouble with their own guys. Too, the boy doing the shooting might face some charges if the brass got wind of what went on here last night.

Staring off into the mist that floated in off the trees, Jim realized he wasn't getting much writing done. Just as he put pen to paper again, a man's form took shape in the fog, and Jim went on the alert once more.

"Don't unsettle, yourself, Jim, it's just me," his sergeant called quietly. "It's my turn to stand watch over this bunch of yokels. You could use some shut-eye about now."

"Hey, Sarge. Thanks, but I don't think I could sleep. I've just been thinking about what all happened here last night, and I still haven't written to my wife. She's been on my mind. I need to be home."

The sergeant smiled and reached into his pack. "This might give you something else to chew on about home. The mail truck rolled in just as I was leaving town. I picked up your letters for you. The other guys can go get their own. A good walk might clear their heads a bit."

"Thanks, Sarge. I appreciate you saving me the trip. Any flack coming down about our favorite cowboy and his target practice in the town last night?"

"Nope. Not a word. I'm thinking the higher-ups will ignore it completely if they can. If someone from town puts in a complaint, they will have to investigate. But I suspect we won't be here long enough for that to happen. There aren't too many citizens left in this berg, and they seem pretty beaten down. They probably will just be happy when they see all of us head on down the road."

"I'll be glad to see us head down the road, too. As long as we are headed in the right direction. I'm hoping to get home in

179

July before those two new babies start interviewing men on the street for a father state side."

"How are they doing? And your wife? I hope you have good news in those letters you're holding on to."

"This one is from my mother. She tells me that it's a boy and a girl. We never talked much about a name for a girl. I've been calling the baby *Junior* since I found out Irene was expecting. Maybe she'll name the girl Hank or something."

Jim's attention to the sergeant grew harder to hold, as the letters in his hands promised to fill a hunger that had nothing to do with food.

The sergeant, sensing Jim's desire to read his letters and find escape from the mud and mess of the German landscape, gave Jim a friendly slap on the back. He grabbed his own wool blanket, and sat himself at a distance where he could keep his eye on the sleeping bunch of soldiers.

The short distance established some privacy for Jim, while his sergeant's presence relieved him of responsibility for keeping watch. Jim, the proud father of a boy and a girl, read his letters from home, finished the one to his wife, and then managed to catch a couple of hours of sleep before they organized themselves to travel once again.

Chapter Twenty-six

June 13, 1945
Ladenburg, Germany

My Dearest:

As you can see, we have moved again today. Not very far, but a little closer to you. Every little bit counts—as long as I keep heading in the right direction. It seems like all the towns end in burg, berge, or berg. As long as the pronunciation is the same, I can't see the difference.

This town is primarily the same as the majority of German towns: Dirty streets, brick houses and a lot of filthy kids running around. The people in this country do not seem to believe in sanitation at all. Not bathtubs, sewers or anything else to keep clean with. Believe me, Honey, some good old clean desert sand would look good to me.

Germany has a lot of advantages for fighting conditions and it is a pretty place, but a closer look makes you wonder. I thought the U.S. had a lot of locks and fences. This place even has barbed wire fences around the gardens. Evidently, the people don't trust each other.

Have been doing a Sergeant's work since two weeks after I got here on a private's pay, but they seem to have too many Sergeants already. The Lt. told me the other day that he is still trying to get the promotion through though. The extra money would come in handy for my family now.

So Pop is still trading trucks. Is he running the station again? Nobody has said anything about it.

Your brother Chuck writes a shorter letter than I do, and that is definitely short.

Must close. The old watch says it's 1:00 and must get up at 6 A.M. so will hit the hay.

Goodnight, sweetheart, I love you, Jim

As it is 1:00 A.M. we have been married 2 years and 3 months.

"All right, men. Fall out. Chow in an hour."

The soldiers watched as the officer walked away, leaving them to look at each other, still a bit shell-shocked, not by artillery, but by the tough inspection.

"I sure didn't expect that," mumbled one of the men from Jim's squad.

"I know what you mean. What's this all about? They have taken all our hand grenades, bazookas, phosphorous grenades and rifle ammunition from us. He jawed at us for ten minutes about turning in our rifles within the next few days."

Jim looked thoughtfully at the ground for a minute, thinking through what they had just heard. He tried to see it from the Army's point of view. "Hey. This might be good news. If they collect our weapons, then we are no doubt headed someplace else in the near future. I know what I am hoping for as a destination."

The squad members chatted on for a few minutes, meandering back to their current quarters. They had landed in a good spot this time. Their squad occupied the entire third floor of an old office building that had, somehow, managed to escape any signs of bombing, shooting or vandalism.

Their floor had a central room that probably served as a conference center. Army cots in the offices and comfortable couches and chairs in the common room gave them a place to relax or to gather for card games, dice playing, or listening to the radio as they traded rumors back and forth. It provided a shabby, but comfortable place to live — but none of them wanted to stay for any length of time, even though it offered lots of elbow room.

As they neared the entrance, an officer's aide came out and called out to Jim, "Hey, Hendrickson, the Lieutenant wants you in his office. Make sure you don't mention his new trousers. He is not happy with them."

Jim nodded, knowing full well that it might be worth his life to say any word at all about the new pink trousers that suddenly blossomed as required daily wear for the officers. Evidently, someone high up decided to show a sense of humor in designing their new gear.

The rank and file men had a good laugh watching their officers walk out that first morning in their pink pants. The lieutenant had announced to all assembled that the *salmon*-color slacks did not make him less of a man, but he admitted that he sure felt foolish. His stern look at the men made them know he didn't want to have to put up with any laughter from them about it.

Jim headed up the front steps to the first floor level where the officers had established their quarters. Just as spacious as the rooms for the enlisted men, this level offered more light from high windows and raised ceilings.

The lieutenant's "office" stood to the left of what looked to have been a reception area. Wondering what the Army wanted from him now, Jim rapped on the door jamb. He could see the lieutenant seated at his desk, his back to the door, gazing out at the open fields beyond, and pink-panted legs wedged securely out of sight under the desk.

"Come on in, Jim."

Jim entered and snapped a salute, still feeling a bit silly himself observing the renewed formalities of military protocol. After so many months in the dirt, snow, mud and thick muck of fighting, a snappy salute with a clean hand felt a bit like playing some kind of child's game. Perhaps the resumption of attention to formality had something to do with the officers' need to restore respect from the men in spite of their pink pants.

"Relax, Hendrickson, and have a seat," the lieutenant said quickly. Lieutenant Kloe had been with Jim's company for some time and the two men had seen action together. Kloe, a good sort, did observe the separation between officers and enlisted men as required by Army regulations, but he never acted as though he considered himself above the men. Not one to stand on ceremony as a rule, even more to his credit as far as Jim was concerned, the man could look you in the eye and you could trust what he said.

The lieutenant glanced down at his desk quickly. It was an old one, probably left over from whatever business had occupied the building when it still belonged to the Germans who worked there. Jim glanced at the papers the officer on the desk, wondering if the reason for his presence was outlined in those pages. He wished the man would tell him up front if any trouble brewed for him.

"I should tell you that this is not a formal discussion. No bad news from home or anything like that, Jim. I just wanted to let you know that I am still working to get you your promotion, and that is long overdue. You've done the duties of sergeant for a good long time without the pay. And now I hear you have two new babies at home using up diapers. You deserve the raise in rank, and the pay that goes along with it."

"Thank you, sir. I appreciate hearing that from you." A small smile pushed up the corners of Jim's mouth. "And I notice you didn't stand up to greet me, either. You wearing your new favorite color trousers?"

The two men chuckled together, both more at ease and willing to laugh a bit at themselves as well as at the Army.

Jim went on, "Seems like we have too many sergeants around here all of a sudden, but no one has been given a promotion for a good long time. I want to go on record though. The boys in the squad I led were all PFC rank or below, just like me. They never caused me a bit of trouble about anything I asked them to do. We toughed it out in the field up to our necks in rough duty, but we watched out for each other. Otherwise I might not sit here today."

"You don't give yourself enough credit, Jim. Those men followed you because you led them well. The men around here respect you, and I've seen them come to you with problems. And you help them solve whatever comes up. You would have made a good officer, and you still could. Have you thought about that?"

"I appreciate the words and the thought. But I've decided that I'm not officer material, sir. I just want to go home, see my wife, meet my new babies before they outgrow me, and take up where I left off before I joined up. When I signed on for this trip to Germany, I wanted to find my brother Bill and bring him home. I got word a bit ago that he got there without my help. His POW camp got liberated when the Russkies showed up. Bill shipped out on one of the first boats back to the states."

"I had not heard that, Jim. I am happy for your brother and your family. I'll bet your mother is glad to have at least one of her boys home."

"She is, at that. Now with Hitler dead and Bill back home before me, I figure my part in the fight is pretty much over. I did what I came for and I did what Uncle Sam asked me to do too. I'm just waiting for the Army to catch on to my way of thinking. If they decide to send me to the Pacific, I just hope it's by way of a long furlough home first."

185

"I understand, though you don't need to spread that philosophy around too much with the new officers coming in. Seems like a whole bunch of folks are showing up over here now, just starting their war time after most of the dirty work is done. They're coming in without any field experience. And too many of them hide behind their rank — don't know better than to throw their weight around, if you get my drift.

"I don't know how long I will be staying around here myself, Jim. But you need to know that there are still loose ends to tie up here. Plus, the boys won't be walking across the water to get home — we have to wait for ships to put them on."

"Well, sir, if you get a chance, just tell the head guys in charge to send back that big old steamer that brought me here. If the Queen Mary can haul us to the war, she can damn sure show up to take us home. That's just good manners, don't you think?"

"Hold on to that thought, Jim. And I'll keep pushing the papers to put through for that raise in rank for you. I'm waiting to hand it personally to someone who will act on it and get it done. That's all, Hendrickson. Go ahead and join the other men for chow. I can smell something that reminds me of bacon cooking out there."

"Yes, sir, Thank you, sir. And it's probably spam you smell cooking, not bacon, just like the color of your new pants."

Chapter Twenty-seven

June 18, 1945
Ladenburg, Germany

My Dearest:

Have been sitting here for the past 30 minutes trying to figure something interesting to write about. Do you have the same trouble Butch? Your letters sounds as if it's no effort at all to put your thought on paper. They sound as if you are right here talking to me. Let me in on the secret and perhaps I can make mine sound less like an obituary column in the L. A. Examiner.

If you can get some film, I'd sure like a picture of you and the twins too. I realize they will have to spend some time in the hospital yet. Don't send anything for my birthday though. I think it's possible to be headed home for the states by that time. Will claim an extra kiss (or two, or three), when I get there. Don't stop writing, though, because I might be here for a good while yet.

I went and saw about that $10.00 allotment today and was promised some results right away. As soon as possible, send me the copies of birth certificates so you can start getting the additional $50.00 a month. I guess you could sure use it now. Don't hesitate to start cashing bonds, Honey, if you need money. I thought you would have to do it long before this.

Turn to the next page of this work of art, and I'll rattle on there... Here I am again with a noticeable change of stationery. Took off with another guy in my squad and went swimming in the river. Today was a nice sunny one for a welcome change. The water is still about 40 below zero, but stayed in for about three hours. Really had a lot of fun getting clean.

The Lt. made me give the boys close order drill this morning, so I promptly took them to the other side of our improvised athletic field and told them to take a smoke. Here comes the Lt. just foaming at the mouth in his pink pants, and he really chewed on me for awhile. To hell with them—I still contend that close order drill doesn't help a bit in a fight and they claim that's the purpose.

Guess the Army will have to either change my mind or give me a discharge. Needless to say, I prefer the latter.

Well, Honey, am looking for the day when all we have to do to talk to each other is to reach over and say, "Hey you, it's time for the kids to be fed."

I love you,

Jim

P.S. They just played "Dearly Beloved" on the radio. Do you remember when it came out? It was when you worked at North American and we used to listen to it on Betsy's radio.

June 22, 1945
Ladenburg, Germany

Hi Butch:

Today you are getting a letter from an exhausted man of the world (ahem). Took one of the G.I. tours to Heidelberg, Mannheim and vicinity. The only reason I went was to get out of drill and training, but am glad I went.

We first visited a huge castle that is now being used for a radio station by Seventh Army Hdqts. It is a huge affair and fairly new. The view from there includes Mannheim and Heidelberg.

We then went to the remains of Heidelberg Castle. It was built in 1310 A.D. and definitely looks like it. You have seen pictures of the old castles with water all around them and a drawbridge for an entrance. This has all of the including the water. This castle has wine barrels down in a large cellar, one of which holds 15,000 gals. and the other holds 49,000 gallons of wine. (They were empty—dammit!) On top of the larger barrel, there used to be a dance floor. The barrels are made of oak and are really impressive.

The place was captured in 1769 by Louis XVI of France and he stayed there for quite some time. They have huge paintings in the place by world-famous painters and original statues of most of the old-world heroes such as Charlemagne, Hercules, Bismarck, the Louis brothers from X to XVI, etc. etc.

The walls in the place are 23 ft. thick and are covered on the inside by silk tapestries, painting and carvings. Heidelberg is a University town and has the oldest and best ones in Germany. Most of the Americans who come over here to study come to these universities.

The old German guide who took us through the castle named off a bunch of the big shots who went through here while he has been a guide. Mark Twain wrote several books at the big hotel right near the castle. The

189

old boy said that the King of England paid his expenses to come and see his coronation. He's a quaint old duck with a handle-bar mustache.

We stopped at the Red Cross in Heidelberg and gorged ourselves on doughnuts and coffee and got back in time to miss retreat—though it rained on the way back.

How's my Honey liking Winterhaven? Mom wrote that there are 150,000 G.I. trainees in the vicinity now. Yuma will, no doubt, be a mess again. They sure had a time when the soldiers were there before. Would like to be one of those trainees in the desert now. They would have an AWOL every other day or so.

Received a box from you today. It had been rewrapped some place along the line and had "Big Hunk" candy bars and dried fruit in it. Sure is good. Have had it for three hours, and believe it or not, there is still a little bit left.

Played volley ball yesterday and some softball. We lost over half of the games, but still had a good workout and a lot of fun.

Had better close as I'm overdoing my usual one page.

I love you.

Jim

How are the younguns doing? Sure hope they are able to get out of the hospital soon.

June 28, 1945
Ladenburg, German

My Dearest:

The "Frisco" conference is over and yours truly still remains on the wrong side of the Atlantic Ocean. This side of the world, in every sense of the word, is monotonous as hell.

We have a new C.O. for our company now. Captain Felton is training a bunch of new replacements that have recently come into the division. They are 18 and 19 years old and haven't seen any combat as yet.

They booked me into being Sergeant of the Guard tonight.

I tried to argue them out of it on the grounds that I'm still only a PFC, but they would not listen.

Funny thing about these lieutenants, they don't listen worth a damn. Will have to see that the boys are in the proper uniform, etc., etc., etc. It's all hooey as far as I'm concerned.

Gen. Eisenhower seems to be getting quite a reception in the states. One of the advantages of 5 stars on your shoulders: You don't have to wait for transportation. If the Army would loan me a rowboat and a set of oars, I'd save them a lot of trouble and row back myself.

How's my family getting along? Am wondering if they are able to come home yet (that sounds as if I expect them to walk home).

It has turned cold again and we are thinking of checking out some long-handled underwear again.

See you soon.
All my love,
Jim

"Turn up the radio. I like that song." Someone sitting closer to the sound box complied with Jim's request and the words to *Don't Fence Me In* began to play. The tune competed with voices of the card players gathered in the common room on the third floor of the old office building.

They had come to the conclusion that, since they no longer had to fight Germans, the Army had set them up to fight the officers these days instead. With nothing much to do but wait to hear orders, their new officers tried to return these battle-weary men, fresh from the hard-scrabble dirt of intense fighting, to the regalia and pomp of military ritual. It didn't sit well with most of them.

Jim entered the common room and raised his voice above the mellow baritone croon of Bing Crosby as he sang with the Andrews Sisters next door on the radio,

Oh give me land, lots of land under starry skies above, don't fence me in,

Let me ride through the wide-open country that I love, don't fence me in.

The room fell quiet at the sound of Jim's voice, and he sang out in his own rich baritone to rival the famous crooner Crosby. As the song came to a close, the dealer at the table led a round of surprised and appreciative applause.

Edgar saw Jim's sheepish blush and tried to take the spotlight off of his embarrassed friend. "I guess that should be our song. It don't seem right. Most of the Germans are back with their families, even though they lost the war. And here we are stuck, following around a bunch of yokels wearing pink pants and issuing orders — guys who never even dodged a bullet. Some luck to be fenced in with officers who want to play games."

Jim picked up on the word luck and used it to change the topic. He had heard and done enough belly-aching about something they weren't going to be able to change.

"You want to talk about luck? I've been carrying a silver dollar as a good luck piece since I got here. My pop gave it to me. It's stamped 1922, the year I was born. I only lost it once before in some straw in a foxhole. Just as soon as I noticed it was gone, we were ordered to move out. You can bet I didn't budge until I found that silver coin. And it was a good thing, too. If I had stuck my head up as ordered, it would have been shot off."

"Yeah, Jim, you need to hang onto that piece for sure. I know you've been offered quite a bit of money for it over here, but nothing can buy that kind of good fortune."

"Well, Edgar, it's come up missing again. I've looked all over for it and I can't find it. If someone swiped it from me, I hope it turns into a curse and he chokes on his chow."

"Let's all look for it. We don't have much else to do. And I don't believe anyone on the third floor would have taken it. We don't deal that way. What do you say, guys? How about a scavenger hunt? First one to find Jim's good luck piece wins the Cracker Jack prize."

The radio got snapped back on as the boys left the card table; some with relief at having something else to do besides lose more money at cards. As they organized a search, the broadcast switched over from music to world news.

A discussion of American involvement in Japan led the stories. A few boys paused to listen and Edgar commented, "Tojo had better start counting his Japs. Who knows how many of them might go missing one of these days. I hope none of us join that search party."

The squad resumed the impromptu "scavenger hunt" and spent time turning over cups, plates, blankets, pillows and any other item not nailed down. Each had his own private concerns to escape, and the search offered a good excuse to move around without going outside in the fierce cold. For Jim, concern about the babies, the knowledge that his father's gas station still remained closed, the decision he had to make about whether to sign up for the Pacific Theater or go nuts waiting to be transported home, all lay on his plate to eat at him.

Soon, the fruitless searching for the missing silver dollar turned into a game of Hide and Seek, with the rowdy silliness that only adult men could bring to the child's game. One man walked to the headboard of a bed, reaching to look under the pillow for the lost coin, only to have his legs pulled out from under him by a soldier who had crawled underneath the bed just waiting to ambush some unsuspecting victim.

All in good fun, the men moved through each room on the pretext of a serious search for the wayward silver coin. Soon, the upheaval and resulting noise brought squads from the other floors in to join them. Jim's silver dollar became a golden quest to rival Jason's fleece, distracting the soldiers from their worries and forced confinement indoors on a dreary, wet day.

Jim had just about decided they should give up on the search for the silver dollar before someone got hurt. The "sneak attacks" on each other grew more reckless as the storm outside grew more intense. He reached in his watch pocket to check the time and pulled out, instead of his watch, the "missing" lucky coin.

His initial reaction of joy at finding the thing faded quickly, replaced by a feeling of dread that tempered relief at his discovery. He knew that if he announced that the lucky coin had been in his pocket all this time, he would never hear the end of it. So quietly, he slipped it back into his pocket.

He stepped outside the office cubicle that served as his bedroom, looked up and down the hallway to make sure no one was watching, and tucked the coin under a section of carpet runner in the hall. Then he headed back to the common room and sat down listening to the rest of the news, waiting for someone else to find it, and if no one did find it, he could "discover" it himself later. He might still be "fenced in" by the Army, but he hadn't let his brains get taken captive.

Chapter Twenty-eight

July 4, 1945
Ladenburg, Germany
8:30 P.M.

My Dearest:

Just about the end of the 4th and am sober as a judge. We were supposed to have a holiday to do what we pleased, but this morning were told to fall out and go to Mannheim for a Division Track Meet. The fellows, including myself, were really busted up about the deal. All we did was ride 28 miles and sit and wait. Was planning on swimming all afternoon and writing some letters.

We had ice cream for supper with some fried chicken to boot. Not bad for Army grub.

Has Hank got home from the hospital yet? How are you doing in the part of the "worried mother?" Somehow I can't realize that we are the parents of two children. I'll sure have a lot to learn when I get back. I'll bet Pop does get a bang out of those kids.

You will probably need that windfall before long if the birth certificates don't get here. Am still working on the messed up allotment on this side. Wish Uncle Sam didn't require so much red tape. Honey, if you need it, you can get hospital funds paid by the Red Cross on my insurance from the government.

Our "training program" is still going great guns. Every day we have the same physical training, close order drill, etc. Perhaps I'll live through it but not without doing my share of griping. And while I'm griping, haven't received any mail from Bill yet and no word from you in a couple of days. Had better write to Bill again. Received a letter from Aunt Lillie and had better answer it—got it three months ago...

July 5, 1945
9:30 P.M.

And so winds up another day in Germany. Early this morning before I could finish up yesterday's letter, I was called to the COs to go represent the company as a member of the "Honor" squad. We won the Battalion show but missed out on the regiment because there was only one man over 5 feet 10 inches tall. Am sure glad we weren't chosen because we would be marching 4 hours a day to keep in practice.

Tonight I went to Heidelberg to see the stage show "Carmen"—G.I. style. The girls in the show were G.I.s dressed for the part. Must say they looked better than these German Fräuleins. They had a good swing band and the show was really great all the way through.

It is raining again and it should be nice sleeping tonight. Think I know where a much nicer place than Germany to sleep would be though.

One of the actors in "Carmen" sang "I'm a Little on the Lonely Side Tonight." He really hit the nail on the head. Sure wish they would let us know something about what we are going to do and how long before we do it.

We are moving Saturday morning another thirty miles or so—a short step in the right direction. With worlds of patience and a lot of military nonsense, we'll someday get on a boat.

I'm going to have to start threatening the mail clerk again. Had him pretty much on the ball for a while, but he is slipping again. Take good care of you for me, Honey. I love you more every day. Guess I used to tease you about a lot of things, though.

If you will always love me half as much as I love you, I'll be content and you may get out the rolling pin if I give you any back talk. You'll never know how much I used to like to tease you.Sometimes (??) you'd get a wee bit sore at the old man and call me conceited—which is probably true. I couldn't write all my feelings for you on a piece of paper, so I just say "All my love" or some such phrase and let the rest go to hell; hoping that you can read between the lines to know what I mean.

I'm afraid I'm a terrible flop at writing a "super deluxe" love letter with onions, mustard, relish and lettuce on it. Would leave out the salt and pepper for a messed up affair. (Talking about hamburgers, I could even eat one of the Lockheed variety right now.)

Talking about something else, I went to a G.I. movie and saw "Son of Lassie" this afternoon. Not a bad show, but the guy evidently loved his dog more than he did the girl. Must have been a damned nice dog.

As you said in your last letter, am getting a little on the windy side— the lonely side too, so will repeat that I love you and close.

Jim

A guy just came in to tell me goodbye. He is going home tomorrow and I would have given half my kingdom in hell to trade places with him.

P.S. Will have you know that I'm not a wolf when I get drunk.

Love,

Jim

The men on the third level of the office building in Ladenburg sat glumly in the common room, watching yet another fall of rain streak the windows, adding more layers of wet to yet another dreary day.

Looking around the room, Jim took note of the faces so familiar to him. He could read their thoughts by their expressions, even in the dim light from the fireplace that had drawn them to seek each others' company. For the first time in his Army experience, Jim had lived with the same men long enough to know their names and their stories. They had shared meals, drills, honors, and sorrows.

The squad gathered in the common lounge to say their farewells to Dale Harms, the quiet man of great heart and small stature who followed a common-sense approach to life. He had shared their accommodations on the third floor, along with some pretty nasty foxholes, before getting to this spot. His cheerful presence would be missed.

The men groused half-heartedly about how lucky the guy was to be released from their enforced confinement. While Jim hadn't been raised in a religion that talked much about Purgatory, he thought he probably understood it clearly now based on what he and the other men endured in the Army of Occupation.

Tired of the direction of his thoughts, Jim broke the silence. "We can be grateful for the lousy weather, I guess. At least the rain meant the Army had to cancel the plans for more close order drills."

Arkie, who could be relied upon to find the sorrowful side of any situation responded, "True, Jim, but that leaves us with nothing to do but stare at the water and wish we were on the other side of the ocean. I don't know how you can keep your eyes open. Didn't you have Charge of Quarters all night?"

"Yeah, and all day too. They finally figured out that I had been dodging that duty. I found one guy missing at bed check. Had to scare up some of our newly-imported soldiers for a detail to chase down the guy's whereabouts.

"It's 10:30 at night and the missing fella was outside in the bad weather gazing into the dark with a thousand yard stare. The poor S.O.B. had just gotten the news that it will be another two months at least before we can expect to go home. It took a while to talk him around to the point where he could muster up the gumption to shower and hit the sack."

Jim looked into the fire, gazing into the flames as the wood crackled sympathetically. Then Arkie, who wasn't one to speak up much, made their ears perk up when he suddenly asked, "What do you think about all these new kids showing up all of

199

a sudden? It's like they are crawling out of the woodwork or out from under rocks. Why bring them over now?"

Harms answered, looking around the circle for confirmation as he spoke. "Most of them I've met up with came over reluctantly. They all had less than six months of duty, and never shipped over. A few who had made it across got sent back for humane reasons. I've always wondered about that. We should all be shipped home for humane reasons. I'm beginning to think that the most humane thing would have been for us to stay home in the first place."

Jim chimed in, agreeing with Harms. "Some of these guys either had connections, or they lived charmed lives. There's a sergeant over here now that got sent back to the Replacement Depot after his first combat experience. But since he is on track to make a military career, they let him sit around far away from the fighting, only to bring him back and put him in charge now that most of the danger has passed.

"Can't say I see much in his character as a future officer though. He's one boy who is liable to get knocked on his ear by yours truly 'cause I don't have a heck of a lot of respect for said person. He probably would fare better working for his daddy back in Massachusetts than pretending he has what it takes to lead a group of fighting men. Maybe he could run for Vice-President or something."

"I hear you, Jim," came from the most senior soldier among them. His high allotment points guaranteed a return to Norman, Oklahoma soon. "We have every right to object to that kind of treatment. You especially as you've been doing a staff sergeant's duties around here for a good long time — and doing them well too. I'll be that with the ratings frozen in the ETO until further notice, you aren't getting the recognition or the pay you deserve either. It's not right."

Arkie spoke up again, with a show of emotion more often kept hidden. "I know Jim doesn't begrudge the extra work he does here. I'm proud to say I have walked by his side." The silence of soldiers embarrassed by open display of emotion filled the room as they avoided eye contact and shifted in their seats.

Harms broke the silence, "I can't disagree, Arkie, even though he spends more time writing letters than any man I've ever known." Chuckles from some of the soldiers brought the mood back to normal in the room as Harms continued, "Now that the war is officially over in Europe, the best among us deserve some thanks. Instead, I'm beginning to see all kinds of game-playing. I never much held for political shenanigans."

"One thing about these fellows arriving who managed to skip the fighting," Jim countered, "I think that ought to get us home sooner. If they just train those Johnny-come-latelies to replace us, we can get on the boats that brought them over here with the spare berths for an ocean voyage back home."

"Sure hope you are right about that, Jim. I feel a bit like that rat that jumped ship, leaving all of his friends behind." Dale shifted the conversation a bit. "I heard that the word has come down to say that no one else will go from here to Japan." The men in the circle nodded. "More than one of us had planned to extend our Army duty in the Pacific, hoping we would get to visit home before shipping over there."

"Yes, Dale, I admit that was my objective," Jim said with a grin. "I reckon the Army realized that there would be quite a number of fellows who would just disappear once they got back to the states. That part of the war should end soon, though. Maybe Tojo feels lonesome now that Hitler is planted under the dirt. And the American forces have started to show that they would like to help the Japanese out and give Hitler some company down under the ground."

Dallas Foreman sat quietly, listening to the dark conversation flow around him, seemingly concentrating on other things. The mention of Japan brought his eyes into sharper focus. "That carrier fleet I heard about while you guys were at the movie yesterday spells trouble for the Japs. There's something big brewing over there. I thought I needed to go there and take part in finishing this war once and for all. Now it looks like the finish for me comes with a lot of foolishness just watching the Germans roam around towns blasted to rubble."

Jim nodded. "I understand how you feel, Foreman. A couple of days ago I walked down towards Heidelberg where that bridge got blown up. You can see the people walk down one side of the water to the only footbridge left across the river. Then they get off the foot bridge and just turn right back around to walk the other traveling the same distance on the other side, back the way they came from. If there was some way, a ferry or a new bridge, where they could cross the river closer to home, they would have a five minute crossing instead of an hour walking to work.

"And we wouldn't have so much pedestrian traffic making it hard to keep an eye on who's coming and going. All this wandering back and forth just makes lots of patrol work for the Americans. So many Germans who just up and left their army when they saw the war was lost, they just show up and don't seem to have anyplace to go. They stand walk around in a daze, most of them just aimless and defeated. Some of them are bitter and hostile, or they get drunk and cause trouble. We've had quite a few casualties in this company — and all after the end of the war."

Jim stopped speaking as Sergeant Harold Grant stuck his head in the door.

"Anyone headed to the G.I. movie this afternoon? It's called *Keep Your Powder Dry* with Lana Turner in it. She is playing the part of a WAC."

"I guess I'll take a gander at it," Edgar answered. "Anyone else seen it yet?"

"Yeah," Dale answered. "I did a while back. The women have too much make up on, but it's not a bad flick."

"Hah!" Jim said. "The only WACs I have seen over here had faces worse than Martha Raye. Make up wouldn't have helped a bit. Lana Turner should be a nice change, make up or not."

Jim dreaded what was in store for him the next day. His sergeant had ordered him to give a lecture on the BAR weapon's care and use. He figured they would get very little out of that since the men required to attend the talk had already used that same weapon countless times themselves. Jim didn't plan a formal presentation. He hoped the sergeant wouldn't attend, even though he would be one of the few who could use the information. If the weather was nice, and the sergeant not in attendance, Jim planned to adjourn the BAR discussion and find a place to go fishing.

Chapter Twenty-nine

July 14, 1945
Ladenburg, Germany

My Dearest:
Today marks a year in the Army and 2 years, 4 months being a married man. Good excuse to go get drunk but haven't the ambition.

It looks as if you are in somewhat of a predicament with both babies finally home from the hospital. And darned if I know what you could do. Know that the twins are too young to travel very far. Guess Kay or Mary could stay with you if you could stand them. Don't know if either one would be much help unless they have changed a lot. Mom said in her letter that she would like you to move over to her house but I am leaving that entirely up to you. I know in-laws can be a lot of trouble, even if they don't realize it.

Can think of no better answer to your problem than for me to be with you. Between the both of us, we could work it O.K. You could take the day shift for a while and I'd take the night shift.

I thought that twins wouldn't be any more trouble than one, but can see that you just get one to sleep and the other starts raising hell—both start raising hell—than you have to start all over again. Wish I could do more than sympathize with you.

One of the guys in the platoon just came in and told me someone swiped his fatigue pants from the clothesline and cut them up to make swimming trunks. Am going to have to run down the culprit...

....Here I am back again. The guy who got the pants was the Sergeant of the Weapons Platoon! I convinced him to give the guy another pair, so all is peace and happiness in the ETO.

Am going to school if they give me the chance. I might learn something and it will keep me occupied for the 2 or 3 months I'll still be here.

Guess Bill is there and having a good time. I'd bet that there aren't 25 people left in Yuma that either he or I still know, though. Sure would like to hear from him.

Must close and take a check to see if the guards are sober.

All my love,

Jim

They are singing "Saturday Nite is the Loneliest Night in the Week." There are seven Saturday nites on this side of the water.

Sunday July 22, 1945
Ladenburg, Germany

My Dearest:

Have not written as much for the last couple of nites and, as usual, have a well-prepared excuse. The 7th Army has been conducting a house-to-house search for the past couple of days, and I've been leading a searching party in this town.

Didn't know that there were so many houses in this area and so much junk in them to search through.

We started the search at 2:30 A.M. and the civilians didn't like the idea or the time of the morning—can't say as I blame them very much.

Our patrol gathered in a few weapons and some G.I. equipment and didn't have any trouble except for one kid trying to hide a couple of pistols on us. I slept from 9:30 last nite till 8 this A.M. after that mess—then found out I am Charge of Quarters for the day—worse luck. Will write again tonight.

All my love,
Jim

Jim went ahead and sealed the letter without fulfilling the promise to write again. He had already gone another eighteen hours with no sleep, and he needed to be fresh when he wrote his wife. He discovered that, when tired, he tended to include things in his notes to her that he would rather not add to her burden. She had enough on her shoulders.

The Army had sprung an ambush problem on them that morning. His squad rose to the occasion, but no one felt too happy about having to go through drills as though they had somehow turned back time to find themselves back in training camps. If they hadn't mastered the ambush techniques by now, they wouldn't be here to simulate them, they would already be dead.

For soldiers who had survived the real horrors of war, going through the motions of a "make-believe" ambush that some new officer with little field work had drummed up was more than just a child's game of pretend. It was insulting.

The mail clerk took Jim's collection of letters and handed him a good-sized stack in return. Jim shuffled through the pile, putting the ones from Irene on top, but stopped and stared when he came to one from his brother Bill.

"Hot damn! It's about time!"

The mail clerk looked up from sorting in surprise. He and Jim shared quite a bit of joking back and forth, and Jim was not usually one to swear. He called Jim his best customer and they gave each other a hard time about the vagaries of the mail service. Jim usually accused him of mistreatment if he didn't get letters in a timely fashion, but there usually were plenty of letters for Jim when the mail did come through.

"What's about time, Jim? Time to go home?"

"No, I wish that were the case. You did a good job today, Mr. Official Army Mail Clerk. This is a letter I've been waiting to see for quite a while. It's finally word from my brother Bill."

"Yeah, you've asked me enough times if I was hiding letters from him. He's the POW, right?"

"He's home now and has been for a while. One year ago this month, I joined up to find him and send him home. Now he's home and I'm stuck here for the duration while my two babies keep my wife hopping. I wish my brother would be kind enough to call out the posse and rescue me."

"Well, that's good news. I'm glad to hear he's home out of harm's way. If he does come after you, he's not as smart as I think the boys in your family might be, though. You aren't completely stupid as infantry men go, but joining up might not have been your brightest move."

"I'm beginning to think that might be truer than you know. I left a pregnant wife who now has twins to take care of all by herself. Now I'm over here playing soldier, practicing up again every day for a war I already fought. It's past time for me to get out of here."

"Your war's not done though, is it? I heard about the search party the other night. You boys still have some loose ends to tie up. And it's dangerous work. It may not be as noisy as the screaming meemies and artillery guns, but that kind of work has its own risk."

"Yeah, I know. I don't tell my wife what it's like to walk around a blind corner wondering if some German fella with a gun holds a grudge to go with it. Some of these Krauts are just waiting for a chance to take revenge on the next dumb American soldier who sticks his fool head into view. There is no way we can round up every last weapon in Germany. And it's hard to tell who among the populace might be a former Nazi instead of a plain civilian. They all speak Kraut."

Jim thanked the clerk again for the letters, warning him not to try hiding any more of the precious missives. He hurried back to his quarters, hoping to have some private time to read them all, starting with Bill's. The lack of contact from Bill had bothered him. He had seen and heard about men released from the different prisons in Germany. Very few of them had survived unscathed, either physically or emotionally. He hoped that his brother turned out to be one of the lucky ones. But then Bill and luck seemed to enjoy a long history together. After all, look which brother had written a letter from home and which one ended up stuck in Germany!

Jim remembered times Bill had lucked out, and a few times when the luck was at Jim's expense. When they graduated from high school, they both wanted to go to college. There wasn't enough money for Pop to send both at the same time, so one would have to stay home and work at the station a year to earn tuition. The idea to take turns seemed fair, so they flipped a coin to see who would go first and who would stay. Of course, lucky Bill won the toss. He took Jim's motorcycle, the tuition money, and a small suitcase to Tempe and enrolled at Arizona State University. Six months later, the family got news that Bill had stopped attending classes. Instead, he had partied away the money, met Skee, married her, and moved back with her parents somewhere back east. That was the last Jim saw of his motorcycle — and his brother too for that matter.

Pop decided that Jim should go ahead and leave Yuma to take one of the higher paying jobs at Lockheed in Burbank, California. As a skilled welder, he would command much greater pay. The plan was that Jim would then be able to earn his own way to college. Then the war began in earnest for the Americans. Bill enlisted and, attracted by the idea of flying, trained as a pilot. Bill landed in a prison camp his first flight out overseas. Jim stayed at Lockheed for over a year before he could enlist. They both ended up in Germany, Bill in prison camp often called *The Country Club* because it was well-run and away from danger, with oversight from the Red Cross. Jim joined the infantry and started digging foxholes and ducking bullets.

Yeah, Bill was one lucky SOB. But on the other hand, if he had been the one to go to ASU, Jim never would have met Irene. So maybe he was the lucky one after all.

Chapter Thirty

July 23, 1945
Ladenburg, Germany

My Dearest:
From your letters, I gather that you have seen the officer material in our family. If he has turned into guys like some of the Infantry lieutenants I know, you can tell him for me that he's due for a licking when I catch him. We have one who actually dug a foxhole down in the cellar while the G.I.s were out in the storm making an attack. He sure is respected in this outfit, you can bet.

Would sure like to read the book "Up Front with Mauldin." His cartoons are pretty good, though not always correct.

They took all our pistols from us today. They tell us we'll get them back when we hit the states—soon. It is midnight so I'd better hit the hay. Bill has the right idea if he is still sleeping his life away. But over here, sleep is not regular.

We are scheduled to have another ambush problem in the morning. It feels like such a waste of time—grown men playing "cops and robbers" again like we did at Camp Roberts.

All my love,
Jim

I ask my mother what she remembers about Bill's return.

"Not too much, really. Bill didn't come back to Yuma right away, though I had heard he was back in the states. I think he got placed in Santa Monica for a while, but then went back to where his wife, Skee, lived with her family. It was in the northeastern part of the country — perhaps Illinois or Iowa."

"Dad writes that he'd heard what a hard time you were having once Rose left."

"Yes, I was in a bad way those first few weeks after Rose left. She had a boyfriend back in Colorado. Bud got sent home right at the end of the war and he wanted Rose to come home and marry him. Seems like all I did those days was wash diapers and hang them on the line. One nice thing though, by the time I pinned the last cloth to the line, the first one had already dried. The dry desert air just devoured the moisture."

"So obviously, you had other things to do than keep track of Bill?"

"Yes, indeed. I recall your father kept asking me about sending the birth certificates. Making a trip to the Red Cross with those two babies took the whole day. Without Rose to drive me, I had a heck of a time. Then, after all the fuss getting there, the folks at the Red Cross told me that Jim had to request the certificates himself. Back in Germany, the Army had told your dad that it would be faster coming from me. I put it off thinking we didn't need the money that bad. I didn't realize that the two babies would add to his allotment points. Not only would he have gotten a higher rank and pay rate sooner, the extra points would have moved up his release date for home.

"But you were asking about Bill. After he had stayed with Skee and her family, the demands from his mother brought him out here for a brief visit. Looking back, it had to be hard on that young married couple to be separated so soon after Bill's return. Jim's mother could be pretty persuasive. I don't recall how long Bill stayed, but I do remember Pop's gray face after he left. He knew Bill wouldn't be back and your grandmother was probably making him suffer a good deal more than he needed to about it."

My father's entire reason for enlisting — to bring Bill home — disappeared with the letter that announced Bill's homecoming. At that point, I see him begin to change even more, with an almost bitter edge I had never picked up on in the earlier letters. His determination to get home and his disgust with the continued demands of the military grew as he expressed the view that there was little real purpose for men like my father in the post war Army.

Mother's memories and Jim's letters supply me with little specific detail about Bill, her energies consumed with new babies, Yuma heat, and a relationship with her mother-in-law that made things tougher. So I did my own research. I found out that "William Clarence Hendrickson" was kept in a large prison camp in Barth, Germany. Built early in the war, it first housed British Air Force pilots, and later, American soldiers as well. Photographs and drawings of the compound show an elaborate collection of buildings, wings, and facilities such as a library, dining hall, and exercise yard — not luxurious, but quite a contrast to the prisons Dad described in the small German towns he and his unit liberated.

The Russians and Allies had some differences of agreement about treatment of the prisoners. Also the issue of who would take responsibility for them caused some problems that were hard to resolve. But overall, *Stalag Luft I* in Barth was a pleasant place as prisons went. Russians called it a *country club*, as mentioned in one of Dad's letters.

At the end of the war, the fate of the men there remained uncertain for a time, as Russian forces had neither the resources, nor the inclination, to take charge of the prisoners' release. Finally, the Americans from the 8th Air Force rescued the POWs beginning on May 1, 1945. "Operation Revival" ensued with an air lift of over 9,000 prisoners of war, with Bill among them.

The Americans flew to Camp Lucky Strike in La Havre, France. After processing there, these incredibly lucky soldiers took priority over the fighting men and were placed on the available liberty ships home. From the timeline, it is entirely possible that Dad and Bill were actually in LaHavre the same time as Bill got ready to go home and Dad settled into the Occupation months.

Bill's lucky streak was going strong for him. He probably left the New York piers, raced through processing, and headed directly to his wife and baby.

Chapter Thirty-one

July 26, 1945
Ladenburg, Germany

Dearest Butch:

Got your letter of the 17th and you are still saying no mail. Am writing an Air Mail letter every day and can't figure it out. I know it is slow reaching you, but still, you should get them.

Am glad you received the birth certificates and will repeat that I can handle it from this end, but you can save 3 or 4 months by handling it in the states.

You have a husband who just turned Republican. The enclosed clipping will explain the sudden change. We walked 14 miles in O.D.s plus ties to see the President. Today we had a bit of Yuma weather and the walk was really a dilly. We stood for about 3 hours and finally were inspected by the President, Ike, and a lot of shiny brass. He knew one of the guys in my squad and talked with him for a bit.

Can bet the 2nd Armored that is in Berlin is having a time. Bet they get inspected by some 4 star brass.

I think they want me at that trial again in the morning. The last session I had was a long drawn-out affair. The trouble with a Court over here is that they have to have everything interpreted by a Kraut. Sure takes time.

Had to drag one of the boys off a Kraut. Can sympathize with the guy's action as his only brother was shot by the Krauts and he took one drink too many and went haywire. Seeing the Kraut POWs turned loose gets most of the boys. They shouldn't make guys who fought with them stay here for the occupation. Bad for the constitution or something.

I could have applied for OCS this week and could've have gotten a commission, but am still afraid I'd have to be in this Army longer if I did. My main interest is to become a lowly civilian.

Received a letter from Bill and Mom. She says Bill seems restless and can't make up his mind what he wants to do with his life. He never knew what he wanted to do anyway, so I don't know why she is worried about that. Sure hope he gets his discharge.

From the way things are going, these wars will be over within 6 months now. Sure hope I am in the states by then. I know what I want to do with my life—spend it with my wife!

Something just went down my neck. A canteen cup full of water! Must go drown an American soldier.

All my love,

Jim

Thursday August 2,1945

Hello ButchO damn it anyway

These Kraut typwriters are definitely the bunk. Three or four of the letters on the keyboard are switched, the back-spacer is in a different place and most of the other letters and gadgets are somehow misplaced. I don't see how the Krauts ever got used to this one, although it is about new. Sure has been a heck of a long time since I've used one of these and you can see that I am having my troubles.

Have just returned from the local hoosegow. A couple of our guards picked up three drunk Krauts that were out after the 16:30 curfew. They are safely tucked away to sleep for the night and will most probably be turned loose in the morning to cause a bit more trouble tomorrow night. It is a great life that we are leading around here.

Signed up for a school that is supposed to be started August 13. Am taking German, Algebra and Physics. I don't think there will be much to it but it will take up some time and get me out of some basic training--getting out of some work is my main objective as you probably can guess.

Your idea of having the twins feed themselves is a good one and you can train them to wash the diapers too. That would probably turn out to be more work than wahhing them by yourself though.

Will send in a request to Rube Goldberg or somebody, and see if they can't help you out on the debl. Does old Barney Rhea still have his stomach trouble? He was sure in bad shape. when I worked for him. Imagine having to eat nothing but vegetables, certain types of bread, no meats at all,and having to take all that junk he used to bring to work. Hope my stomach is O. K. when I get away from this Army grub.

Can guess how the weather is in Yuma about now. It has really been cold here for the past few days. I miss my daily swim in the river. Am wearing a field jacket and my O.D.'s and am inside a room with all the doors an-d-windoWs closed. One day we burn and the next daI we freeze. The fellows are really complaining about the mail situation now. Some of the mail reaches the states in about ten days and some of it takes six weeks. It is getting here a little faster than that but not much. Will have to take it up with my Congressman.

Rather than get any madder at this typewriter than necessary, I'll use the pen. At least it doesn't belong to the Krauts. From my descriptions, you probably think a lot goes on around here in the way of entertainment. We have picked up our share of SS men, weapons and loot, but for the most part it is just a drunks or something similar a person could find in the states.

The newspapers are causing a lot of trouble over here. According to them, the wives in the states are raising hell, stepping out on their husbands, etc. There is also usually an article about G.I.s fraternizing with German women or going with French and Holland girls. That will add 500 divorces for guys over here. Wonder what in the hell the papers are trying to do. The score is up to 6 divorces in my platoon alone. Last night one of the guys got a letter in which his wife gave him the air. He got drunk and made me read it. He hasn't even looked at a woman here and claims that his wife just took it for granted that he was stepping out.

There are lots of guys who run around with the German women, but they would do the same thing in the states. Same goes for the women in the states. Guess the papers are running pretty short of news when they stir

217

things like that up. This particular case burns me up because I've been with this guy since I've been over here and he is really a good egg. He is the one who went on pass to Holland with me, and during the fighting he saved my skin more than once.

Got pretty well wound up on that, so will close.

All my love,

Jim

August 7, 1945
Ladenburg, German

My Dearest:

Received your letter of July 31 and one from Mom today. Glad to hear that Lockheed is still paying off. Did they ever have that strike that you spoke of? Heard today that Major Bong was killed in a test flight of Lockheed's new P-80 jet propelled plane. After knocking down 40 Jap planes, he should have taken a nice desk job someplace.

We had some excitement this afternoon. A fire started in the attic of our cook shack and they called the Kraut fire department. Our officers wouldn't let us put it out because they figure the Krauts knew what they were doing. They got here about 30 minutes after the fire started and really went to work.

We never saw anything so funny since we have been this side. Every guy was in a fancy uniform and they all ran around like a bunch of monkeys in a cage. Every time they got their hoses all connected and the water turned on, one of the hoses would bust and get a couple of them wet. One of the guys took some pictures of the affair and has promised me some of them. The fire didn't do too much damage, and we really had fun watching it.

They are opening an enlisted men's club for the battalion and plan on having doughnuts and homemade goods. It's a good idea if they have a good man to run it and it should go over well with the guys. We have a beer hall, but all the beer is Kraut beer, and that tastes like water. They get a Kraut band to come in and play once in a while, but all they know is the "Beer Barrel Polka" (and that gets tiresome as hell.)

From the way I write, you might get the idea that I don't care much for the place or the people. Guess it's just that I'd like to get home and see you and the kids so much.

Actually, we are living like kings in comparison to the foxholes. As you often say, maybe we will both never be satisfied about our lives. Never heard either of us griping too much when we were together though.

The hours are slowly but surely passing away. I tell myself every time I look at my watch that I'm that much closer to home. If this new atomic bomb is a success, perhaps it won't be too long before all the Japs have the honor of dying for their Emperor and we can all come home.

All my love,

Jim

What kind of steak are we going to have when I get home?

"I don't know what the Army is thinking. This basic training is like being back in my first day of camp! I can't take much more of this."

Jim looked at the soldier doing the complaining. He had rarely heard a cross word from Arkie. You could always count on him to do exactly what he was told without any griping. If Arkie was whining, you knew things had gotten bad.

"You know what's behind, this, don't you Arkie? The Army can't get liberty ships fast enough to send us home. First they tried giving us extra guard responsibilities, but there are only so many Germans with weaponry to confiscate out there. The problem is the rise of venereal disease. The medics complain that it is all they treat these days. So, there you go — if the boys would just keep their pants zipped, we wouldn't have to practice how to be soldiers all over again just to keep us busy."

Arkie looked at Jim, wide-eyed. "You mean to say that the Army thinks these stupid drills and simulations will force us to act moral? That's just insulting."

"Well," Jim answered, "the USO shows and movies sure aren't keeping the men occupied. Like tonight; here we have Jack Benny as master of ceremonies of a great show with

Martha Tilton, Larry Adler, Ingrid Bergman and the like. That was the first time I knew that Jack Benny could ever play the violin. Now how many men do you reckon will go see it?"

"I'm going. I want to see that *Casablanca* skit with Benny as Bogart."

"As for me, I have to get my clothes all ready so I can be up to snuff for the CQ job again tomorrow. But where is the rest of our unit?"

"Oh. They went on the prowl in town."

"Yep. That's about right. And if you believe that they went looking for educational opportunities, you need to stay far away from used-car salesmen. They went looking for women; no matter that some of them have real nice wives or sweethearts waiting for them back home."

Early the next morning, the clerk called for the men to line up for mail call.

"And Foreman, you have a package."

The news was welcomed with a cheer. One of the older men quipped, "Remember, Private Foreman, it's better to give than to receive."

The rest of the men waited patiently for their names to be called, but many of them left empty-handed. After so long in Ladenburg, the news back and forth became a bit sparse. But even occasional letters from home added a bit of a break in their routine.

The last letter distributed, the men began to disperse. The clerk called out as they walked away, "Try to catch a news broadcast if you can. I was listening to my radio this morning before I drove in, and I heard there was some major action in the Pacific today. I think America may have dropped one of those atom bombs we've been hearing about."

Not long after, the third floor common room of the old office building in Ladenburg Germany hosted more men than it had ever seen at one time. Drawn in by a radio that worked pretty well, men from several squads gathered by the warmth of the fire and stayed glued to the signal as they waited for news.

Foreman brought along the care package from his wife. Guzzling coffee and making short work of home-made chocolate chip cookies, the men listened anxiously for a story about the bomb and possible Japanese surrender. Grave voices of commentators who struggled to mask any sign of emotion waivered with repressed emotions as they reported the meager facts available on the August 6th bombing of Hiroshima.

It was too soon to hear detailed stories of the damage, but descriptions of the potential for devastation from the science experts left the men hollow-eyed and thoughtful. The announcer reported that experts seemed to think that the Japanese would call it quits before the week ended.

The news broadcast finished, and music began to fill the room, cheerful and bouncy, in jarring contrast to the serious faces and somber expressions of the men in the common room in Germany. Without discussion, the soldier closest to the radio snapped it off, and silence replaced the offending noise of the tinny music.

Arkie got up and refilled his coffee cup from an urn set up to brew the strong, dark beverage made from a precious bag full of ground roast beans that came with the now untouched cookies in Foreman's care package from home.

Jim broke the gloomy silence first. "That new atomic bomb must be a rugged thing for the Japs to cope with. One of them would easily wipe a town the size of Burbank, California, right off the map."

"Do you men think the Japs will really call it quits? I can't see them giving up so easily. They have been a stiff-necked bunch of folks so far." Jim's friend, Edgar, took another cookie from the care package, but kept it in his hand without taking a bite, perhaps too full from the enormity of news about this new destructive force America had introduced to the world.

Bill Campbell, the medic for their unit, raised his serious face. "That would really be a swell deal if the Emperor did surrender, and we could all get out of this damned Army. What we did over there sounds awful enough to put an end to the fighting forever. That being the case, then it might have been worth it. I sure don't like to imagine it, though."

No one argued with him, and the quiet resumed as the men dealt with their own thoughts. Each one had a huge stake in events they had no control over. Tired of rumors, tired of waiting, tired of living in a strange land, they all wanted to go home. But they sensed that, with this bombing, the world had changed and home would never be the same.

One by one, the soldiers picked up their mugs and left the room, returning to the semi-privacy afforded by their separate sleeping quarters, a luxury the Army seldom had provided before this Occupation post. Soon, only Jim and his good friend Edgar remained, watching the glow of the fire, but both seeing something behind their own eyes and beyond the flames. Then they, too, moved quietly to their own space and their own thoughts.

The next morning dawned, cold and crystal clear. Looking up at a rare and cloudless German sky, Jim had difficulty imagining what the sky in Japan must look like in the aftermath of such a powerful blast from the new bomb. He had yet to see any pictures of what a mushroom cloud looked like, but it had been described to him. Here in Germany, the morning filled with a chorus of birds and the air felt fresh and bright.

One by one, the soldiers came out from the office building that served as a temporary home base. Carrying coffee and lighting up the first cigarettes of the day, they gathered in small groups, trying to make sense of the sparse news reports available so far.

Sergeant Grant joined them, looking up at the sky without comment. Then he barked, "We have to go search the town again. An officer in the battalion has gone missing. Seems the officers threw a big party last night at the colonel's quarters, and the captain left early, drunk as a skunk. No one has seen him since. So grab chow in a hurry and start your squads on the search grids."

They thought that the guy had probably just taken in too much booze, and then found a place to sleep it off. But that first clear day of searching quickly turned into four days of rain, with a cold wind to add a share of misery. The captain did not reappear.

As they walked their grid again in the town of Ladenburg, Jim and his men wondered if the news of the bombing had reached many of the Germans whose doors they knocked on. The houses surrounding the towns had once been homes for solid, working-class German citizens. Now, the smell of cooked cabbage wafted tiredly through the streets, bringing with it a miasma of defeat and indifference.

No one had any news about the captain, and they didn't seem to care much about that or anything else the Americans could bring to their front steps. They were indifferently polite, not warm or welcoming, evincing little interest in happenings outside their own houses. Jim figured they were waiting too — for the Americans to leave.

As they tramped down the muddy streets, cold water running down their necks, Jim commented to his search partner, "Sure glad I didn't send off for civilian shoes. I don't think I'll bother at this point. I've gotten used to these Army boots now. I might as well keep them until we leave Germany. Then I will leave them behind — German mud and all."

His buddy, Edgar, looked at the mud-caked boots. He smiled at the sight of the worn footwear and wet weather, commenting, "You'll also be leaving with some more money in your pocket. Congratulations on that raise in rank, Jim. It's long overdue."

"Thanks, Edgar. I'm glad it finally went through. Don't see as how it will make much difference, other than a little bigger check. Maybe enough to buy my wife a lollipop or something."

They both laughed at that picture. But being reminded of the new rank gave Jim a bit of a spring in his step as his boots, still lined with at least three pairs of sox, sucked at the mud of the German streets.

Sunday August 12, 1945
Ladenburg, Germany

My Dearest:
Enclosed are a few snapshots of some of us. It's hard to get all the gang together to take a picture. The general opinion is that the war will be over in a few days. We got in our kitchen and sang until 2:30 this A.M. I was a little under the weather, but not too bad. Didn't get up for breakfast this morning.

That old Captain that went missing finally showed up this morning. Seems he wasn't that drunk after all, just got depressed by the news for some reason. It doesn't pay to dwell on things too much like that.

I sewed on some stripes last night and guess I'll never hear the last of it. They really ride me about them around here. Told them I'd put the whole bunch to doing K.P. but it didn't make any difference.

I sure hope they make a recount of the points in the near future. If they do, it won't be long till I'm out. I still have not decided what I'm going to do when I return. The main objective now is to get back to the states— and to you.

How are the twins doing? They are just about 3 months old. Am sure hoping to get some pictures of them and you.

Must close,

Jim

Jim finished Irene's letter and looked over the photographs before he added them to the envelope. She should have quite a collection by now and he figured she stood a better chance of finding a safe spot for them than he did considering his limited storage over here.

This last bunch of pictures showed something Jim figured to be fairly unique. In one shot, the German Fire and Water Department members stood all lined up in fancy uniforms. Other less formal pictures showed them in action, battling the blaze with limited efficiency, but with a flair for the drama they seemed to enjoy as part of their duties.

After that cook shack fire died down, more on its own than from the efforts of the German fire brigade, the Americans and Germans had worked together to clean up the aftermath and repair the damage.

Jim had gotten to talking with a few of them. They knew more English than he knew German, and they seemed like all right sorts, though their pompous uniforms and exaggerated sense of self-importance made him chuckle a bit. As they chatted, Jim had brought out his silver dollar lucky piece.

He had practiced a trick of putting that silver coin on the back of his knuckles, tossing it up and grabbing it out of the air. He could line up three coins on the back of his hand, toss them high, and capture each one of them in three successive air grabs. Seems a fellow could occupy his idle time on guard duty with some of the silliest games, but Jim thought the Germans might laugh a bit to see his coin trick.

One of the Germans asked if he could look at the silver dollar more closely, and Jim handed it over. The fellow put just the one solid coin on the back of his own hand, and tried to imitate Jim's air grab. Instead of catching it cleanly, he knocked the coin about ten feet away. They all watched with horror as the coin rolled down the partially cobbled street and wobbled on down the curb into a sewer drain.

Jim stood, frozen, while the Germans all yelled and scrambled toward the drain, falling over each other as they tried to stick hands down the opening. The sound of the clinking silver diminished rapidly, echoing faintly from far below the street level.

Jim felt a sickness in the pit of his stomach. He said, "Damn. The Krauts took my luck after all."

The German firemen stood in a circle, glancing at Jim as they jabbered in their own harsh-sounding tongue. Whatever English they had mastered abandoned them in their obvious distress. The fireman who dropped the coin hung his head in abject misery. The man standing next to him punched him repeated on the arm, obviously berating him for his clumsiness. Jim recognized the word *dummkopf*.

Jim watched quietly, still feeling queasy and sad. When it began to look as though the German was in for some serious trouble, Jim shook himself out of his frozen state.

"Hey, how about seeing if we can get down there and find the coin before it gets washed away or something? Isn't there a way down into these sewers?"

The Germans looked at Jim, and then at each other. One of them touched the shiny brass buttons on his firemen's uniform and then petted the top one thoughtfully. Then, with a snappy command in German, he shouted out to his brigade. One by one, they removed their fancy jackets and headed out into the middle of the street. A man-hole cover, spread thick with so much mud its surface was barely visible, offered surprisingly little resistance as the Germans wrestled clumsily to get it open.

Three of them took turns to drop below the street level, disappearing into the dark below. The others ran back to the sewer opening where the coin had disappeared. Calling out a steady chatter to guide the firemen below, they took out torches and aimed them down the hole where the coin had dropped. Below, the sound of the three intrepid explorers could be heard, calling out their progress. Jim suspected some of the calls included swear words he didn't recognize.

He watched them, thinking that the Keystone Cops could take lessons from this bunch. With little expectation of recovering the coin, he tried to tell himself that it didn't matter all that much. The piece his dad had given him didn't really have any special power. After all, it was only worth one American dollar, silver or not. He really didn't hold with superstitions. But still, he hated to see the thing stay in Germany. He didn't want to leave it, or any part of himself, behind in this unhappy land.

One loud shout quieted the Germans quickly. They must have decided to halt the futile search, and Jim waited to see the searchers surface from the hole in the middle of the street. The first one who popped his head up was a filthy mess. When he reappeared above the hole into street level, he looked like a creature in a horror film coming up from a swamp, covered with muck from head to toe, and dripping unimaginable filth as he rose from the dark hole. But there, in the German's clenched fish raised high over his muddy smiling head, Jim spotted a flash of silver.

When Jim held out his hand for his lucky piece, the German held it behind his back, smiling. He and his two buddies all extended one muddy paw, palm up and open to Jim. They repeated something in German, laughing out as they spoke.

Jim got the picture. He realized that they wanted him to buy the thing back from them, to barter for it like a child's game. He had to laugh at their nerve. He appreciated their efforts to go after the coin, but after all, one of their men was responsible for it going down the drain in the first place.

He pulled out a pack of cigarettes and matches from his pack and offered them to the dirt-caked men. The one holding the silver dollar handed it over and all three shouted *Schönen Danke* as they headed off to their water truck.

Jim mumbled a quiet *Bitteschön*, thank you, under his breath, but he really didn't begrudge the German's their bribe. He was just glad to have his luck returned to him. Holding the photographs from that day to put into Irene's letter, he wished that he had a camera of his own. He sure would have liked to take a photograph of the "rescue" to send to Irene.

Instead, he had spent the next couple of days chiseling and cajoling negatives from other G.I.s who had taken pictures at the fire. At least he would have those so that he could remember the time he had worked with the Germans to recover his luck in the muddy streets of Ladenburg.

"Jim!" Edgar stood and snapped him a smart mock-salute in the third-floor common room, spilling cookie crumbs all over the floor around him. "You're back from the movie already? That had to be one quick show! What happened? Was it a war documentary?"

"That's *Sergeant Jim*, to you, Private and don't you forget it. I earned those stripes to match my job promotion."

Edgar's mouth dropped open in astonishment, until he caught the give-away glimmer in Jim's eye. "Ah, man. You had me going there for a minute. You wouldn't be the first soldier in this Army to grow a big head over your new rank, but you would be the last one I would expect it from."

"Maybe so, Edgar, but if you got into that fudge Irene sent me while I was at the damn flick, you would find yourself on K.P. duty for the rest of the Occupation. That's a promise."

"Nah, I wouldn't have done that, Jim. I've survived this war by being smart enough to dodge the German artillery, I'll be damned if I'll risk life and limb for my sweet tooth; though I wouldn't be the only sad sack in this man's Army to make that kind of mistake." Edgar looked down and brushed some remaining crumbs off of his fatigues. "No, I finished off the last of the cookies my ma sent. Irene's fudge is safe from me. For now, anyway." He smiled with a rakish grin, waggling his eyebrows.

"Speaking of 'sad sack of a soldier,' there's going to be one sorry fellow in this outfit when we catch up with the man who left us sitting in the dark waiting for a movie that never started. The projectionist didn't show up! About twenty-five or thirty men sat there twiddling their thumbs for about the last half hour."

"Sorry about that, Jim. That's a bad deal. But it's not like the guys had anything more important to do around here."

"Yeah, I'm going nuts." Jim sighed. "I joined upon the offer to take classes. German and Algebra. I guess I might as well learn something while I'm sitting around. Maybe it will get me out of some of that guard duty."

"They've cut back on the drills since the Japanese bombing. No more of us will be going over to the Pacific either, so that time was wasted anyway."

"The Army is running out of ways to keep us occupied in the Occupation. Kind of funny, that. But I always did hanker for more schooling. You know, my brother, Bill, won the coin toss when we were out of high school. His luck sent him off to ASU, and he spent the tuition on parties instead. Flunked out, took my motor bike, and headed off without a word. One thing I plan to do in this life for my kids. They are going to have a chance at college if I have to work five jobs when I get back to save the money."

"You'll do it, too, I'd bet on you, Jim. Now how about a taste of that fudge? Then I'm going to hit the hay and continue to catch up on all the sleep I've lost over the last two years."

"Sure, why not. If I share it, I won't get fat. I'd hate to go home to Irene looking like a Lardo."

Chapter Thirty-two

August 22, 1945
Ladenburg, Germany

My Dearest:

Received your V-J edition. It was on our anniversary then, even if it was unofficial. Can picture the hell raised the night after the proclamation. The war won't be over for me either until I get home and out of this Army.

Sure is nice to know that no more G.I.s will jump off again. Over 300,000 will not know that the war is over and it is one hell of a price to pay for peace.

Am still looking for quite a bit of trouble with the Japs. They are calling the surrender a "truce" now, and that doesn't look too good.

I don't think you'll be worried about my being backward when I get home. It may be a bit strange to be home, but you are very easy to get along with. They make a big cry about "readjustment" of the G.I. to civilian life, but I think the majority have very little trouble.

(Am more than ready to try).

So Yuma's Chamber of Commerce is calling the town "Greater Yuma" now. They might as well say "Greater Winterhaven" as far as I'm concerned.

That is one crazy song on the radio. I'm listening to the Andrew's Sisters sing about how you get no bread with one meatball.

Goodnight sweetheart. I love you.

Jim

August 23, 1945
Ladenburg, Germany

My Dearest:

The planes are still grounded because of bad weather, so I'm still gonna gripe about the weather or the mail service, or both. Enclosed is a clipping of the Division shipping list. Figuring 120,000 men to a Division, and they plan to ship 250,000 monthly from here, that will get us home in 2 or 3 months.

Also, if they lower the point discharge score to 75, in 4 more months of service duty and one month in the states, I'll have enough to get that highly prized piece of white paper that says, "Discharged." (Oh Happy Day)

Sent you a map of the Division action over here showing the different campaigns we were in. Also sent that book of Heidelberg in the same pkg.

The 86th and 95th Divisions are really raising hell about being shipped overseas again. Can't say as I blame them a bit since there are a lot of fellows still in the states that have never been overseas.

Have just returned from a show, "Without Love" starring Katherine Hepburn and Spencer Tracy. It drags a bit, but on the whole is a very good show.

Came back to find that I am Charge of Quarters again tomorrow.

You know damned well that you would get an argument if you wanted me to sleep on the couch because of it being too hot in Yuma. It may be plenty hot in Yuma, but I don't believe there is any weather anyplace that would make me sleep on the couch if you were around.

They are playing "Sentimental Journey" on the radio and would sure like to be taking one to the states. Patience, patience...

We will have been engaged three years. (Please count a couple of years and 7 1/2 months of married life in those three though) I well remember the night, but not very much about the Palladium. Remember we weren't engaged until about one o'clock the next morning.

Will always cuss that Van Nuys cop out for giving me a ticket when I went looking for the rings. Guess he could see I was thinking of other things at the time.

Can truthfully say that I love you more now than then, and I was really in love at the time.

Must close and write a letter to Ray and Mollie congratulating them on the new arrival. Then I have to pull a couple of hours guard to cover as one of the boys came up missing.

All my love,

Jim

September 5, 1945
Ladenburg, Germany

My Dearest:

How is my honey tonight? Not as lonesome as I am I hope. Today I moved to new quarters and am taking over another squad. I know the guys in it pretty well, so it's O.K.

I also feel better about the coming home situation. They are counting the points next week and that will put me up to 66. I should be among the first to leave as soon as the points are counted according to the Division scoreboard. That second baby gave me the extra I needed. The twins will probably be eating steaks by the time I see them form the progress they are making.

September 6, 1945

A day later, and I now have a problem squad to handle after all. Two thirds of the fellows got drunk, and they probably have been doing that every night. They are continually fighting.

Have had two guys go to the aid station in two days I've been with them—one with a broken arm and the other with a deep cut under his eye. Two more are under restriction and my assistant squad leader pulled a knife on one guy. (Result—one battered face on the asst. squad leader)

I was awakened at 3:30 A.M. by one guy insisting I get up and take a drink with him. This Kraut wine sure makes some of the guys do crazy things.

A new ruling came out that you can bring only one pistol home. Makes me sore, but maybe I can smuggle the extra one I have through though.

The first Sergeant says we must make a bed-check on the Company so I'm off for now...

...Back with pretty good results. Only two men gone tonight. That is much better than average for this outfit. Saturday nite, half the Company is gone and not much can be done about it.

Give my love to the twins and take good care of you, honey.

Jim

A shiny golden coin in the sky over Ladenburg brightened the September morning, but the sun did little to warm the chill of brittle cold growing stronger as the hours ticked slowly by. Jim opened his pay envelope to find $60.00, twice what he had been getting. He figured he would hang onto it in case he got the word to ship out. If the return trip home was anything like the trip over, he would need some cash on him for traveling across the states. And if it got any colder, he would need to buy an extra blanket.

The base emptied daily as more men with the revised threshold of sixty-five allotment points got their alert to leave. Jim had just given his men the news that he had been reassigned to new duties, leading the third squad in the platoon. He hated leaving the second squad. He had worked with them since he joined this outfit, and they had become more than fellow G.I.s. Looking at the new pay envelope, he realized that every good thing had a stiff price tag over here.

Jim planned to join some of the old guys tonight to help a few of them celebrate their alert. He figured he had better get a letter written today in case he got too tipsy to write. More likely though, he would occupy his time watching the other guys drink. But then again, he might just join them this time. He hadn't relaxed enough to risk any serious drinking since he had left New York. Jim still didn't take to the drinking the way so many of his fellow Army men did, but he thought it might take the edge off of his sour mood.

He decided to take a walk to try to clear his head of cobwebs and warm his bones up a bit from sitting in the cold. The river lay not two blocks from their office/garrison, and he headed to the walkway along the water at a quick pace, enjoying the sun on his face and the loosening of muscles as he walked.

Paths on both sides of the river rose above the level of the banks. These provided a peaceful place to stroll, but he maintained his long-stride and speed to warm himself against the cool air that wafted gently landwards from the rippling water. The level of the water had receded, and he decided to leave the established pathway to risk meandering closer to the water's edge.

Growing up in Arizona, Jim had spent many hours attempting to escape the desert heat in the waters of the Colorado River, a winding and sometimes shallow body of water that served as the boundary line dividing Arizona from California. Floating in that river on an inner tube, swimming across the water to the other side, fishing along the banks or jumping in to chase the fish in the cooler wetness — those were activities that made a small-town Arizona kid feel like the king of the world.

Today in Ladenburg, beside this colder and much less friendly flow, few people graced the paths on the walkway this side of the river. Most folks who used the paths had already taken this route to their day's work. Jim enjoyed his solitary reign over the cold banks under the bright sun.

He cherished this rare slice of solitude away from the constant commotion caused by so many war-weary men living in small quarters. Glancing at the shore line as he walked closer to the water's edge, he eyeballed the bank to see how much the water level had dropped. Then he spotted something in the mud by his boots that caught his interest.

He picked up the grey metal object that poked up from the sludge, out of place in the long stretch of wet brown earth, and sure enough, the distinctive butt of a German pistol came squelching out of the mud with a sucking swoosh.

He took it to the river and rinsed it carefully, sloshing the cold water over the piece, checking to see if it was loaded. He thought to himself about all the other souvenirs he had gathered in this foreign land that he had to get rid of before his anticipated trip back to the states. This one might be worth taking back home. He would get tired of carting all the other junk, but a pistol would be something to hang on to if he could.

Of course, he also might be forced to get rid of it before he got to the States if the Army took notice of it. Or it might have to go over the side of an ocean liner if one of his superiors found out about it. But he wouldn't leave a gun here for someone else to use. Who knows, some kid might pick it up, or some bitter former German soldier. Germany was already shot up enough.

Chapter Thirty-three

September 12, 1945
Ladenburg, Germany

My Dearest:
The mail drought for awhile has evidently been broken. You say you received four letters and today I got one. I wouldn't trade it for anything. I am still hoping for some pictures. The new squad says they don't believe me about having twins and the prettiest wife in the world. If I can keep these guys busy and sober, I might be able to keep them alive until we ship out of here.

Last nite we had a little excitement for a change. A bunch of Negros came in town and started raising hell. The Captain went out after them and didn't catch them, but I'll bet they don't come back because the guys pumped a lot of lead in their direction when they ran out. They will be scared for a while, and Ladenburg will be voluntarily off limits to them.

The Negro soldiers here are really in an awful mess. They fight with the Krauts and get in a lot of trouble. If they do try any of the same tricks in the states, I'm afraid they'll run into some ex-G.I.s who will have no regrets at all when they exterminate them. They probably feel just like that about us.

How time passes!! Only 9 hundred and one years, a month and a day, have passed since I took off from L.A. and left you with Daisy Belle. I hear that Tojo tried to commit suicide. Too bad he didn't make it and save a lot of expense.

I received a box today that you sent some time ago with 2 pipes, hair oil and a book in it. The pipes are really honeys and I'm the stylish cuss now. Thanks a million for the package, Sugar, but you needn't have spent so much money. Hope I don't forget and sit on them. Am smoking now, and the room is kind of cloudy.

I'm Sgt. of the Guard tonight and will probably be up the greater part of it hunting the guards. I have already been out twice today in a jeep hunting for them, and these boys are elusive. More of the fellows are leaving tomorrow.

There has been a Kraut in here for an hour trying to get permission to buy some roofing for a house. There is a legal aspect and I doubt very much if he gets anywhere with it. If we stick around long enough, maybe we will rebuild everything for the Germans.

Honey, I'll write and tell you I'm coming when I have cause. I'll have notice before I go. Am not sure whether or not I can write once I'm on my way.

Perhaps I'll be able to talk Mom out of her neurotic condition as she always did listen to me, but there is no use trying to do it in a letter. I have tried and it only hurts her feelings. She was burnt up at me for the time I wrote about Pop's operation, and I don't think I was wrong in writing the letter, thought I heard about it later from 3 different people.

I read a sob story in the papers about Mickey Rooney over here and how he hasn't seen his child. He sure hasn't got a thing on me and a lot of other fellows. I sure would like to see those babies, and refresh my memories of you.

My memories of you are just as clear now as eighteen months ago, though I would like to be able to see you and have fresh memories.

All my love,

Jim

"Sergeant?" Jim did not look up immediately at the call from the door. Then he remembered that the boys in this new squad didn't call him *Jim*, and he looked up to see one of the new guys standing there, waiting for his attention.

"Sorry, Private. I've been doing a sergeant's duties as just plain Jim for so long, I don't answer to my rank just yet. I wasn't ignoring you, son." He spread photographs on the bunk in front of him as the soldier settled himself on a neighboring cot. "Take a gander at my twenty-four points! I just got these pictures from my wife that I've been bragging about."

The soldier grinned, pleased to have a glimpse of the twins and their mother. "You've gotta shows these around, Sarge," he smiled, "the fellows have been wondering if they were just something you made up in your mind."

"Yep, I will as soon as I've looked at them often enough to convince my own self that they are real." Jim gathered the pictures up and put them aside, glancing at them now and again as they talked, just to reassure himself that they were still there. "What is it you need, son?"

"Some of the fellows found a bunch of German ammunition and a signal gun. They have started shooting flares. They look sort of pretty, now, like fireworks. It wasn't so long ago we didn't care for the sight of them, and for good reason." He stopped for a moment, clearly reliving the fear those night flashes had caused to the men in the foxholes. Those pretty lights often preceded a machine gunner, tank attack, or a few rounds of 88 artillery fire that sometimes brought death to their dug-outs. Shaking away the memory of the fighting, the soldier concluded, "I just thought you ought to know about it."

"Thanks, we'll see what the brass wants us to do. No doubt they have noticed the lights in the night sky. But it might be a lousy business if the boys start mixing liquor with the fireworks. Whatever they found could cause a lot of serious bodily harm."

Jim took one last glance through the photographs before he stowed them safely away. Then he sighed, put his boots back on, and went out into the German night. A three-quarter moon glowed brightly, but up in the sky the occasional burst of light stood out in eerie relief over the river at the other end of town.

He was glad to see that whoever discovered the cache had the sense to shoot the things off over water, not houses. He looked up at the sky for a while before heading over to the platoon sergeant's quarters. He would probably have to wake the man. Heading in that direction, Jim was aware that if he could walk 8,000 miles in that direction, he could join Irene. He wondered if she saw the same moon that night. He knew she wouldn't be seeing any flares.

IV: The Homecoming

Chapter Thirty-four

September 23, 1945
Ladenburg, Germany

My Dearest:

Just received the best new since I heard of the twins. Am supposed to leave Wednesday September 26, 1945 to join the 12th Armored Division to leave with them for the U.S.A. Rumor has it that yesterday's news broadcast said they leave here for the states October 15th. Allowing plenty of time for Army Snafu's, that will put me in Winterhaven around the 15th of November, though I think it will be sooner than that.

As soon as you receive this letter, don't write to me until I let you know. Will continue writing to you though, and will try to let you know exactly when I will be back. Our Captain is also leaving with me and about 14 fellows from the Company including "Pop" Adams. The next weeks will be hectic ones if they are anything like coming over.

I'm going to close for now and do a bit of sewing on more stripes. Sure wish you could sew them on for me.

All my love,
Jim

Ladenburg, Germany
September 25, 1945

My Dearest,

At 5:30 in the morning, we are on the first leg of the long trip home. 8000 miles is a long way, but am hoping to be with you in 6 weeks.

I sent you a discontinued correspondence V-Mail this morning and still have a lot of packing to do. It's surprising how much junk a guy can pick up. Sure have a lot of it and expect them to issue me some more.

The weather looks like it's going to snow. Hope it holds off until after I get out. We will probably spend the next month in tents, but believe me, it will be worth it to get home.

Did I tell you, I got my silver dollar back after bribing the Kraut fire and water department with a pack of cigarettes and 3 cigars? They went right down in the sewer after it for something like that is worth a lot of money to the Krauts.

We got rations today and am well-stocked on cigarettes and pipe tobacco for the trip. Hope I get a chance to pick up a good present for you if I go through Paris, which isn't too likely.

Must shave and finish packing so good night, Sweetheart, and I will be seeing you soon.

All my love,
Jim

The day had finally come. Jim stowed his gear in the transport and waved a final goodbye to his squad and to the boys still left behind. These soldiers had rousted themselves out of bed early, still on the back side of dark and two hours before chow, to see him off and give him a final good-natured salute.

He looked at the office perched like a grey ghost above the night-shrouded street of Ladenburg, the closest thing to a home he had known for so many long months. He would not miss it. But the boys — he would miss them. They would represent the only part of Europe he would regret leaving behind.

Pop Adams perched beside him, sitting on a soft pack that held tents they would sleep in once they got clear of civilization. The trucks filled up, and Jim spotted some familiar faces, but no men he knew by name. Others in the back of the truck slept on, not at all interested in seeing who else would join them on their journey.

Jim settled into his spot on the truck, grateful that they would not have to walk. He had fully expected a convoy like that Red Ball Express he'd heard about from some of the men, with their quick march into battle so long ago. His train trip to Belgium was a different lifetime.

Pop Adams had stayed up most of the night, packing last-minute items and dithering over what to leave behind. No one in their quarters had gotten much sleep with all his cussing. So now, as the truck found its way into gear and begin to lumber along the rough road, Pop settled in to join most of the other men on the truck who had decided to grab a snooze.

Jim stayed awake, watching out of the openings of the truck to catch the first light of a day that would take him just that much closer to home. He came to grips with the idea that he would not see too many familiar faces for the rest of the journey. He and Pop had joked about how they seemed to be "joined at the hip" for all the war-related traveling. Jim had joshed Pop a bit, telling him he was glad to have his ugly mug to look at. It wouldn't matter to him if he had to travel with strangers, as long as he was headed home at last. But still, he gladdened at having Pop to share the ride.

In spite of the recent weeks of enforced inactivity, Jim had done little deep reflection on his war experience. These last few months at Ladenburg had been filled with anxiety of many kinds. There was the sheer fatigue of search for German prisoners, the continued worry about those men for whom he was responsible, the fear that he or any one of his men might open a door to a German farmhouse and face the barrel of a gun. Those dangers diminished slowly as the Americans established control of their conquered towns.

Even though the risk of possible bodily harm had gradually lessened day by day, uncertainty and loneliness had replaced those adrenaline-rushed days of survival, spreading a listlessness and lethargy that sapped the spirits.

Jim had watched a lot of his men crawl into bottles of liquor to drink their way into numbness. He managed to avoid that trap and fill his time just keeping busy, holding his deepest thoughts at bay, inhabiting the world described in the letters to and from his wife. He rarely had uninterrupted time alone for deep thoughts.

He looked around at the strangers on the truck. A mixed bunch by age and rank, this group represented men with high allotment points from about every outfit in the ETO. Jim thought about his own allotment points. With credit for time in the States and overseas, combat awards, and dependent children, he decided that someone had done him a favor by sending Irene twins. That probably cut his stay short by several months. He would be sure to thank her for her contribution.

The driver of the truck suddenly drove off what passed for a road through the German countryside. Jim watched him hop down from the driver's seat and disappear on the far side of the truck bed along the road side. The jostling woke Pop

Adams up and he snorted from sleep with disgust. "What's going on, Jim?"

"Don't know, Pop. Let me find out." He jumped out of the truck, thinking maybe the driver had just got taken short, needing a fast nature call. But he found the driver staring down at a map, looking puzzled and shaking his head. Glancing up at Jim, he commented, "This wouldn't be the first time I got lost, but I sure as hell better figure out where we are supposed to go quick. If the rest of these men wake up and realize I'm headed in the wrong direction, they just might pull out one of their illegal souvenirs and shoot me."

"You must have done this before a time or two. Can I help?" Jim looked at the man closely with a feeling that he knew him, but doubtful of how that could be possible.

"Sure. Thankee kindly." The dark-skinned man kept his nose buried in the map and did not look up at Jim's face or meet his eyes. "Take a gander at this map, would you? We're supposed to pick up some folks at Division Headquarters, and then push on directly to Ulm."

The two men stuck their heads together in the brightening morning. Jim sure was glad he had been watching the terrain. He was able to spot some of the landmarks, familiar to him as he had traveled much of the area around Ladenburg in a Jeep, searching the countryside first for Germans, and later for soldiers gone AWOL.

While he pored over the map, he also consulted his memory for when he might have seen the driver before. No African-American gentlemen were numbered among the company of his troops. Once, when he had gotten separated from his men back in the Ardennes Forest, a jeep driver from the non-white squadron had rescued him and taken him on one hell of a rough ride, the two of them fighting their way together out of a tough situation. But this man was not that soldier.

Still puzzling about his mystery, Jim returned to the map.

"I think this is where you left the route. We were supposed to make a turn about five miles back. Once you do that, we will be on a better road heading towards Mannheim. Right now, you're on the wrong side of the river, but there's a bridge that's not blown where you can cross just beyond the turn you passed."

"Thank you, Sergeant. I'm a good driver, but maps don't help much if you don't know the local landmarks. I wish the Army would just let me do my usual job. I'm a mechanic, not a navigator."

Jim laughed. "The Army wants us to obey without question, but I think that's just because they don't want anyone to realize they don't have the answers either. I've learned that the only difference between enlisted men and officers in the Army is that the officers are the ones who won't ask questions. Their orders come to us bull-head foolish, heading us in the wrong direction, no matter who gets hurt."

"Yeah, that's so. At least I stopped and asked. I enjoyed the chat, soldier. You'd be surprised how often I drive all day without sharing a word or a thought with my passengers. But say, Sergeant, you do look familiar to me."

"I've been trying to figure just where in the Sam Hill I know you from, fella. You put me in mind of someone, but you're not from Yuma, Arizona, are you?"

"No. But that's solves it for me. You're Jimmy Henderson, aren't you? We met up at the recruiter's back in Los Angeles. My name's Hugh."

"Dang it all, Hugh. It's Hendrickson, not Henderson. You always did mix that up, but so do a lot of folks. Remember, we were going to look each other up? I'm glad to see you."

"Me too, Jimmy. I'm glad to know you are all right and heading home safe."

"Yessir, that's right and it's about time. Speaking of time, I spent a good part of my time in training camp trying to find you before I figured out that they didn't mix the men by color in the Army." The two men stared at each other, grinning ear-to-ear. Then they clasped a firm handshake.

"I've thought about you from time to time, too Jim. Good to know you're all right after this party the Germans invited us to."

"Thanks, Hugh. And I'm glad you are still willing to shake hands with a white fella, even though you still seem to have trouble finding your way around without my help."

The two men laughed out loud, and Hugh headed back to his place in the driver's seat. "Best you hurry and get in that truck, soldier. I'm likely to leave you standing here by the side of the road."

Jim slapped the side of Hugh's door, and headed over to climb into the back of the vehicle, chuckling all the while.

Back in the truck, Jim laid his head against a rolled blanket. He examined his recollections of Hugh before their Army training had begun. He remembered that he had looked for him for quite a while, not realizing that the colors of their skin would keep them from marching side by side as brothers. He was glad at the strange coincidence that brought the two together, if only for a brief moment of connection.

As Jim drifted off to sleep, he thought about what his job might be in the months to come. Whatever he found at home to do, it would not have anything at all to do with killing people — he knew that for certain. Once he climbed up that gangplank to get aboard the ship, he wanted to leave all of that behind him, right along with the mud and stink of Germany.

Chapter Thirty-five

Ulm, Germany
September 27, 1945

My Dearest:

Well honey, I'm through with the first leg of my journey. We got up at 4:00 A.M. yesterday and went to Battalion Hq. then to division Hq, and then traveled till 8:00 all last night on trucks. We got lost a couple of times and were wet and muddy when we finally arrived.

Nothing was ready when we got there, so we just found a floor to sleep on till the A.M. Got some cots today and will make it O.K. till we leave, which will be about the 2nd of October.

I have been checking the guys' clothing all afternoon and not much else. Everything is in quite a turmoil, and will no doubt be that way until we finish processing.

It's colder than hell here and a misty rain has been falling all day. I can take a lot of this, though, as long as I'm headed toward home and you. How are the kids doing? Are they still refusing spinach? I'm missing those letters of yours.

Have been separated from most of the guys who came with me from our company. We will all meet on the boat though. Must close and hit the sack.

Am trying to get out of taking over one of the platoons (am not at all lazy) but don't know if I'll succeed.

All my love,

Jim

October 1, 1945
Dittingen, Germany

My Dearest:

Just a line to let you know that I'm still on my way. The situation has changed a bit now and the latest is that we will move from here by October 7. I will sail October 20 if all goes as planned. (That never happens in the Army though.)

We have been organizing the company. There are now 240 men in it and we are ready to take off at the earliest opportunity.

The weather has been cold and wet around here. The food is good and there is plenty of it and we have a good place to sleep.

I'm on my way. (Oh joy)

I certainly miss your letters and sit around dreaming of things we can do when I return. Boy, I can hardly wait. It has really been a long time since I first woke in the morning to find I was in a United States Army Camp and not with you.

Miss you more and more now that I don't get my daily Sugar report and hear how the twins are doing lately.

Must close now for chow. I love you and will see you soon, though to me it will seem like forever.

Always,

Jim

"Line up, men. Roll up your sleeves."

A group of soldiers reacted to such an order with stoicism and quiet. No one said anything out loud, but the unspoken disgruntlement in the room bounced from wall to wall. One by one, they stepped up for the inoculation, not knowing why or what substance the syringe injected into their bodies.

"What, no lollipop?" Jim commented on his way out the door. A couple of the men walking with him smiled just a little. One of them remarked on the logic, or lack thereof, of giving soldiers immunizations before they got on a ship together bound for home.

"I guess we need that so we won't take German germs home with us," Jim continued. "That almost makes sense to me. I wish they had a shot to give us so that we could leave all the *memories* of Germany behind."

Jim glanced behind and spotted Pop Adams coming out of the line, rubbing the spot on his arm where the needle had jabbed him. "Ouchy. I think those Army needles are big enough for my Aunt Eloise to use for knitting a sweater. Dadgummit, that hurt."

"Hey, Pop. Haven't seen you around for a couple of days. Missed the sound of your griping." Jim thought how ironic it was to run into Pop at that precise moment. He had just commented on leaving every memory of Germany behind, but here was a man he would want to remember. He would never have met him if he hadn't crossed the ocean. "How's it going, Pop? No need to ask if you are provoked about all the delays."

"We're just spoiled after all that time in Ladenburg, Jim. We forgot how much fun it is to jump in and out of trucks and sleep in the dirt."

Pop reached in his pocket for a cigarette and Jim pulled out the new pipe from his wife had sent. He enjoyed carrying it around these days. The package had been sent weeks ago, and had just caught up with him. He liked the ritual of filling the bowl of the pipe from the tobacco pouch, tamping it down, and sometimes even getting it lit.

He never would have been able to do that when they were in the field. The pipe, for Jim, represented a return to civilized behavior with the leisure time to complete an action without any worry that a bullet or artillery barrage might interrupt.

"Did you hear about the strike in New York, Pop?"

"Yeah, we have a radio we can listen to over in our section. Those fellows in the New York harbor probably don't realize how they are holding us up. If the boats stay in New York, we can't get on 'em from here."

"I read about the strike in a newspaper one of the officers left out. The article said it started with the elevator operators there a month ago. The finance district nearly had to close down because the executives on the top floor didn't want to climb stairs. Then the strike spread to other workers like the dock yards and longshoremen."

"Yeah, Pop, I agree. Working folks need to stand up for their rights, but it sure seems like a hell of a time to have them flexing their union muscles."

"I just want to get home, Jim. If they don't hurry and settle, we won't be going anywhere any time soon. And this place doesn't exactly offer any of the creature comforts I would like to get used to again."

"I know, Pop. I just can't stop thinking about clean sheets lately. Not a real bed in sight here. I don't know what I'd do if a sheet floated out of the sky and landed in my lap."

"The Army would probably take it from you anyhow, Jim. Not G.I. issue."

"Hey, what do you think about getting out of here? I'm planning to commandeer a jeep or something and head back to visit the guys in Ladenburg. We're stuck here with nothing to do and it's only a 200 mile trip. I'd love to see their faces when we waltz back in just to say howdy."

"Hell, yes. Let's do it. Sure beats sitting around here with a bunch of strangers. The folks here just don't smell right. Where's that truck?"

Chapter Thirty-six

Ballendorf, Germany
October 16, 1945

My Dearest:

Received four very nice letters from you tonight and they helped my morale 100% Since they have taken British ships from us, nobody seems to know how that will affect our shipping out. Am sure it will hold us up for at least an additional two weeks. They seem to have messed the redeployment situation up with the strikes, etc.

My trip back to the Company didn't turn out so good. Our truck broke down and we had to hitchhike back and were late getting here. It's pretty cold to be hitchhiking in Germany now, and it's about 200 miles.

The old Company is pretty broke up now as everybody is getting transferred and new guys are coming in. Our Captain back here was sore as hell about our not showing up on time, but he can go to hell as far as I'm concerned.

I got a kick out of the clipping you sent of "Marriage Clinic." I am not worrying about our married bliss as we always managed to get along good except when I'd start teasing you. I had a good time during our one year together, and can see no reason why we can't have even a better time when I return. We can sure try anyway.

And another thing—you talk of reforming—believe me, you don't need it.

Am still counting on Thanksgiving dinner with you and hope it's sooner than that.

I love you.

Jim

My 50 cent pen isn't worth a damn.

October 22, 1945
(Still) Ballendorf, Germany

My Dearest:

It is a cold, wet morning on this side of the pond. How's the weather in California now? We just had a billet inspection by one of our schoolboy 2nd Lts. He got mad as a wet hen when I didn't call the squad to attention as he walked in the house.

Any time I do that it will be a cold day in hell. Some of these officers are certainly going to be in for a surprise when they are civilians and have to go to real work. There are a lot of 2nd Louie's, nineteen and twenty though, who are damned swell guys and know what the score is.

They are playing "Can't You Read Between the Lines." It is the first time I've heard it and it sounds O.K. Radio is a wonderful thing to pass away the time with.

We are supposed to be transferred into an Ordinance Company in the next couple of days, but it will just change the name of the outfit as we now plan to stay in this town until we ship.

They are sending some Navy ships to offset the loss of the "Queen Elizabeth" and the "Aquitania." According to the latest dope, that will put us on the boat Nov. 10. Oh Happy Day!

I sent a money order for $90.00 to Pop to fix up the car. I thought that would be the easiest way to settle the score there. Still have over $200.00 and will send you a money order as soon as I can get it.

They only let the guys send one money order per month now, and I didn't get one off in September because we were on the move. If I don't lose it, I should have enough to show us a good time when I get home—and buy you a lollipop besides.

I love you and miss you more every day. One consolation is that the number of days is growing shorter.

All my love, Jim
To hell with this pen!

October 28, 1945

Dearest Irene:

On the move again and am now in an ordinance Company. There are rumors, and very strong ones, that we will be transferred to the 36th Division. What a life!!

Am thoroughly convinced that no honest effort is being made to get us on our way home. Am getting madder by the day at all the moving and technicalities that keep us over here.

I think they are trying to get the guys sore so they will reenlist. A lot of fellows are going AWOL and they had better do something fast or it will get worse.

I received a letter from Mac and see that he is at the old Burke Mansion as a civilian. He evidently doesn't know what he is going to do. A long time ago he and I were talking of going into business together.

He still seems to like the idea. Mac has a good head on him and is reliable, so we might make some kind of deal. He has saved up quite a bit of money and who knows? Maybe we might make a million!

Getting back to the dreary present tense, I miss you like the devil and still hope that the Army pulls a miracle off and gets me home by Thanksgiving.

Miss the daily letters no end, honey, and will try to write often so you can hear the latest mishaps on my return home.

All my love,

Jim

November 1, 1945

My Dearest:

We are finally moving out—but only to the 36th Division. No one seems to know exactly when the 36th is going home, but we do know that they are through processing and are all ready to pull out. Look for me about the last of November the way things are now. Boy, I'm certainly getting impatient to get started.

Everything is going pretty good over here now. We have the usual guard, K.P. and minor details to look after, but we're not overworked. Have been playing football for quite a while and we actually won a game this morning 30-0. It's getting colder now, but there hasn't been too much rain so it's not at all bad.

I'm wondering how your brother, Sparky, is coming along. Whether he got out or not? Guess Chuck is discharged by now too. Looks like I'll be the last sonofagun to get home. Guess I should be thankful I'm alive though, at that.

Just heard the news and the aircraft carriers are supposed to be here Nov. 10. We should have one of them.

How are the kids doing—foolish to ask in my letters now, but I sure miss your letters about what they are doing and the worries you have with them. It's going to be nice to see you soon instead of a letter though.

Have to check my pistol out and see what kind of transportation we are going to get to move in. Will write as soon as I get to the 36th.

All my love,

Jim

"Well, Pop, I've got to say that I'm glad that you and I still have each other's ugly mugs to look at in this outfit. But I'm beginning to have nightmares that the Army is going to send you to Yuma with me. I don't know that Irene would cotton to that."

The two friends sat in front of their quarters in the small town of Blaubeuren, Germany. Though not in the same squad any longer, they still managed to find each other during the day and check in on how the other fared.

"Speak for yourself, Jim," Pop replied, "I've always thought you were a handsome fellow, at least you used to be before you stopped getting letters from your gal back home. That black scowl on your face has frozen you ugly as German sauerkraut!"

"Hah! That's my own fault. I told her to stop writing because I figured we would be home before her letters caught up with me. I sure wish I hadn't done that. But that's not the only reason to frown around here."

"I know. That captain is hell on a heap of hogwash. I overheard the lieutenants talking. They said he is a German-Jew who sweated out the war censoring mail in Paris! You'd think he would feel a bit more strongly about the reason we fought this war, but he seems too centered on himself for any kind of social conscience."

"I believe that. He doesn't seem to have any idea what the fight we just got through was about, though. When he called the whole company out for formation right after our arrival and then gave everybody a chewing out for not having pressed uniforms..." Jim stopped, at a loss for words, just shaking his head with frustration. "He had no excuse for that. Some of the men here, like us for example, have been with five or six different outfits while we are waiting to go home. We've slept rough most of the time, hopping on and off those trucks with just a heck and a holler for warning."

Pop's face began to take on the scowl he had accused Jim of wearing. "Expecting men to press their shirts under those circumstances. That's just wrong."

"I don't think our dear captain will get too much cooperation out of the company from here on out. I just hope we move out of here right quick, before I get in trouble with him myself. The way I figure it, I've been eligible for discharge since November 1. If I thought I could find my own way home, I would demand that discharge now and just start walking."

Jim and Pop Adams looked up at the two-story "home" provided as their assigned quarters in what had once been, before the war, businesses and office spaces. On the bottom level, hanging above a former German cafe, some clever person had hung a sign that said, "Kraut Kaffee and Koffee."

On the second floor, a window opened. One of the men from Jim's new squad called out to him. "Hey, Sergeant, is it time for chow yet?"

Jim looked over his shoulder at the cafe. Part of their billeted compound, it provided a comfortable and efficient means of feeding the men while they stayed in town. With no need to set up a separate cook shack, the men enjoyed the homey atmosphere of the restaurant-style eatery instead of the mess hall or road side K-ration dispensary. Even though it still put Army food in front of them, the more relaxed atmosphere improved the flavor somehow. Jim eyeballed the front of the restaurant for a moment, and spotted movement as a man from the work crew came to unlock the door.

"Good timing, Soldier," Jim called up to the man waiting in the window. "Time to put the feed bag on."

Turning back to Pop, Jim gave a nod towards the door of the cafe. The two men rose together and headed on over.

"Guess we should find something else to jaw about, Pop. At least we've got good food. And eating on real plates at a table sure beats the hell out of K-rations sitting on the cold dirt or at the back end of a truck."

"You usually find a way to look at the plus side of things, Jim. And I'm with you on this one. They've got real eggs for breakfast instead of that powered crap. Now that's something to smile about."

Chapter Thirty-seven

Blaubeuren, Germany
November 9, 1945

My Dearest:

We had our first snow last night and it is winter again in Germany. I was definitely hoping that we would be on our way before now. All they are promising us now is that we'll be home for Christmas. Enclosed is a clipping from the "Stars + Stripes," which our General claims is false and that our shipping date is still November 20. I don't think anybody knows for sure.

Enclosed you will find a money-order for $90.00. Why don't you buy yourself a blue suit or dress with it and call it my birthday present to you. There is still some chance I may be home on your birthday to take at look at it—and you.

I really got drunk the other night. My platoon Sarge and myself went to the NCO club and really did a good job. Our Jewish Captain came around at 9:30 the next A.M. and really gave me hell for being in bed. Great life if you don't weaken!

I haven't written to anybody but you for two months and am too disgusted to do so. We are the well known "Victims of Circumstance" over here. This 36th is quite an outfit. They believe in keeping you busy ten hours a day. We are subjected to calisthenics, close order drill, hikes, lots of inspections, and an almost continual string of confused and conflicting orders.

Oh how I love the Army. Guess I have become a sarcastic sonnavagun.

I find myself continually wondering how you and the twins are managing, and just how long they are going to keep me here. Must close and find when our dear Captain is coming around for his usual inspection.

I love you and will do my best to get home to you as soon as possible.
All my love,
Jim

Closing Jim's letter and folding it neatly back in its envelope, Irene looked over to one crib and one wicker laundry basket where her two children slept — for once at the same time. Jimmy, still the smaller of the two, nestled comfortably in the basket, and Ginger snoozed peacefully in a child's crib with sturdy side rails.

Pop Hendrickson had brought her a letter, mailed to his house because Jim didn't have her newest address. She had settled Pop in the one easy chair with a cool drink. He sat dozing in the still-warmish heat of another desert day in Irene's small living room. Come to think of it, this really was Pop's living room. He had just moved her and the twins into it, charging her a small amount of rent. She refused to live there without paying something. Her pride and her husband's honor demanded that they not take charity, even from family. Pop had told her how much he admired her independent spirit, and truth to tell, his family could use the income too. Pop still had two girls in Yuma High School.

Irene thought for a moment, blessed by the rare quiet, deciding how much of her recent letter from her husband should be shared with Jim's father. It worried her to read that Jim had actually gotten drunk. He had never been much for the booze, not that she knew of anyway. It would probably worry Pop too.

As for getting cross with his captain, that had to be a first. Everyone Jim worked with, at Lockheed, and in the Army so far, had admired and respected Jim. Always the "go to" guy, people just naturally liked her Jim, and he would find a way to get around someone who didn't warm up to him. She knew that wasn't just her biased opinion. This captain must be some piece of work!

She looked at the $90.00 money order and shook her head. Her husband must not have any idea about how much a woman's clothes cost these days, but she couldn't imagine anyone paying even half that much for one dress — or even a suit. He wanted to see her in a blue dress, though, and she would surely make that happen. Then the rest of the money would go right where it would do some good — in their joint savings account.

She felt very proud of the way Jim complimented her on managing the money. "I guess," she said softly to herself, "you get a good head for budgets when you've never had any spare money to worry over." Her thoughts rested fondly on her own mother who fed eleven children from her own garden, with regular contributions from the cows and chickens in the yard. They might have come through the hard depression years wearing clothes made out of flour-sacks, but they never did go hungry.

Pop dozed on, his mouth slightly open, not quite snoring, but breathing deeply in a raspy and regular rhythm. Irene walked over to where the babies slumbered, looking at the two of them and enjoying another rush of pride. They sure did look beautiful. Ginger's blonde wisps of hair had begun to take shape in airy curls that framed her face like a fringe of laughter. Baby Jimmy looked a bit frail yet, with his sandy-colored, barely-covered scalp damp in the heat, moist tufts of brown locks plastered in swirls to his tiny head. Prettier babies, she never had seen.

She mentally subtracted another $10.00 from Jim's money order, determined to arrange for a formal portrait of the twins.

Close to five months old, she decided she needed to record more of the babies' first months for her warrior husband. He had missed so much of them already. When he got home, they would have outgrown infancy. Those precious first days were lost to him forever.

Irene, not one to indulge in self-pity, straightened her shoulders and swallowed the sigh that had nearly escaped her lips. She could stamp her foot in exasperation at the Army, but it would wake the twins. She decided she needed a moment with their Grandpa before the twins woke up and walked briskly into the living room where he immediately stirred at her entrance. Irene suspected that he had just been pretending to doze to give her privacy with the letter he had brought.

"Sorry Rene, I didn't mean to fall asleep on you. So how's Jimmy doing?"

"Well, Pop, he sent me a whole lot of money here. Looks like he won't make it by December 8th after all, though. He wants me to spend the money to buy myself a birthday present from him. I won't be spending it all. It's too much money."

"Now, Sugar, you deserve every cent of that money. You should splurge on yourself. Jim's no fool when it comes to money, and I know he wouldn't send it if he needed it for something else. I'll take you shopping any time you say."

"You are so good to us, Pop. I didn't know how I was going to manage after Rose left. But I couldn't keep her here once her beau got home from the fighting. He wanted her back in Colorado. He wasn't about to come out here to Winterhaven."

"No shame on her boyfriend for that. Rose went where she needed to be — with her man. Now I know how hard this has been for you, and I want you to know how proud I am of you. And I'm proud of my son for having the smarts to pick such a good woman to be his wife."

Irene rose from her perch on the coffee table and gave Pop a kiss on the cheek. "You want another cold drink while I'm up?"

"No, I have to be getting back to Kittie. She will be fretting about where I've gotten off to. She knows I was headed here with Jim's letter. And you can be sure she will demand a full report from me, too. It was all I could do to keep her from opening your mail. We haven't had a note from Jim for a while now."

"I know, he mentions that he just has been too disgusted with the Army to write. He knows I'll share the information. Here, let me write down the parts about when he thinks he's coming home."

Irene takes a pad and pencil out and writes, first from memory, and then copying passages from the letter itself. She looks up at Pop to see him staring off at the children. He has a soft, gentle smile on his face. For a moment, Irene can see an older version of her husband's face predicted in his father's profile.

"You know, Grandpa, those babies of ours are going to be very spoiled if you dote on them too much. They must think that you are their daddy by now."

"Well, I'm a poor substitute for the one they haven't met yet, me with this cane and gimpy leg. I sure hope I can get back on two strong feet before Jim gets back. But I'd rather he got here tomorrow and watch me limp than have to wait any more. It must be driving him crazy to have to sit around wondering if the Army is ever going to get him home."

"That's pretty much what he says in the letters." Irene looked thoughtful and a bit apprehensive. Then, her face settled into determination to have her say. "Pop, you don't think I'm horrible for not handing the letters from Jim over to Mom H, do you?"

"No, honey, I don't. I've tried to explain to her that there are things between a young man and his wife that don't need parents looking over their shoulders." His eyes twinkle with mischief. "You may have noticed that your mother-in-law spends most of her time thinking of her own needs and feelings. I've often told her she has a terminal case of the 'wants', and she does. But I love her and I try to make her as happy as I can. You're a good wife to Jim, and a good mother to his children. You don't have to dance to her tune, so don't worry a bit about it. She'll come around."

Not entirely convinced by Pop's long stretch of logic, Irene still gave Pop a smile. "Do you want me to wake the babies so you can have a proper visit with them?"

"No, I do have to get going. But I wanted to ask you one more thing, and I want you to think about it. This place you are in right now has been ok while the kids are little, but I'd like to get you settled into a nicer place with a bit more room before Jim gets home."

"Oh Pop, you are just too good to us. I think we'll be just fine here, though."

"Hear me out, Irene. Your sister-in-law, Virginia, is heading out next week with her Eb to live in San Diego while he finishes his hitch in the Navy. That leaves the place up on Eighth Avenue empty. You know, the house that you said seemed built sideways?"

Irene chuckled at that. "Yes, Pop, I know the one you mean. You told me you planned the house that way. I still think it needs a front door on the front of the house instead of on the side."

Pop nodded.

"If you are up to the work again so soon, I'd like you to pack up and we'll move you in. That would give you time to settle before Jim gets home. Then, once Jim gets back, you two can take your time to find a place of your own or just stay on here a while. I could rent it out to someone else, but I'd rather see your small family settled peacefully close by. What do you say?"

Irene thought about it. The house Pop intended for them sat on a nice yard in a good neighborhood over on the Arizona side of the river. She would prefer to live in Yuma than in Winterhaven. And she loved the house Pop offered to them. It had wonderfully thick walls that stayed warmer in winter and would remain cooler when summer returned with a vengeance. With three bedrooms and an extra large kitchen, she and Jim could really spread out. If they did return to Burbank, it would be easy for Pop to find new tenants or let Virginia and Eb have it back when they returned.

Strange, but pleasing to her, the house sat sideways on the lot, so the front entrance didn't show from the street. With a back yard and side yard, she would have plenty of safe play area for her two children, plus room for a clothes line. The laundry she had to do for two babies took up most of the room in this little bungalow and a place decorated every day with drying diapers did dampen her spirits. The oddly situated house on Eighth Avenue had strong appeal.

"Pop, you are a heaven-sent blessing to us. Yes, I'll start packing, but on one condition."

"What's the condition? I have a suspicion I know what you are about to say, Irene, and I won't take a cent more in rent from you. That's final."

"Now Pop, you know me too well. And you don't want Jim to feel like he is on charity, even if it is from his own Dad. We

271

will pay you exactly what Virginia and Eb have been paying. Plus, I want you to bring Mom H and yourself over for dinner every week."

"I suggest a compromise. Make it every other week so you can come to us the other weeks. Your mother-in-law does enjoy cooking for the family. Is it a deal?"

"Yes sir," Irene said and gave Pop a smart salute and then a hug. "Wait!" she cried, stepping out of his embrace, "Jim won't know where to find me when he gets back if I move again while he isn't getting letters."

Pop chuckled, "Well, honey, he doesn't know where you are now either, does he? But don't kid yourself, Irene. If I know my son, he would find you in a fidget and a flash no matter where you were. We Hendrickson men let nothing get in our way when it comes to our women."

Irene watched as Pop maneuvered his leg into the car and drove off down the dusty Winterhaven street. Just then, one of the twins cried out softly from the basket. She knew from the sound that it was baby Jimmy, hungry again. And Ginger wouldn't stay asleep long if he was awake. The little blonde girl already had made it clear that she wanted to keep an eye on her brother at all times. The two of them were starting to become a team, though they didn't look at all alike. So with a brisk stride and a cheerful grin, Irene returned to her twins, wondering how Jim would manage to weave himself into the fabric they had spun without him in his prolonged absence.

Chapter Thirty-eight

Blaubeuren, Germany
November 14, 1945

My Dearest:

In one hour we will have been married two years and eight months, and I have been away from you about half of that time. We are going to have to make up that time in some way. I have a suggestion or two, but perhaps had better not put them on paper.

I sent a box to you yesterday which contained a lot of odds and ends of souvenirs, etc. Also included was a bottle of perfume for you and a razor for Pop. Sure hope the perfume gets to you O.K. as I had a devil of a time getting it.

Our latest news is that we start moving out of here November 20 and should get on a boat at the latest by December 1. Here's hoping—again! They still are promising us to be home in plenty of time for Christmas.

I read "Forever Amber" and it is by far the filthiest book I've ever read. I don't see how a woman or man would have the imagination to write a book like that. It is about a girl in England who sleeps with a new man every other page and doesn't leave out many details. It even mentions how he plays with her breasts, undresses her, etc. etc. etc. And to top it all, she even sleeps with the King of England right after Oliver Crowell's time. She, of course, has her real lover and two children by him. It is a book that will sell a lot of copies though.

Honey, my thoughts are only to see you and the kids, and I can't write a whole letter on that. This whole mess has been one delay after another, and you can tell it is getting to me more than the fighting did. I am homesick, but not for the states or a home, just for you.

All my love, Jim

The sound of the piano filled the hall and bounced around the walls of the NCO club in counterpoint to the ping pong balls tapping on a pretty good table. Jim and a few of the other sergeants brought their beers over to the lounge area, and sat down together to listen to the performance, waiting for a turn at the game, or for the truck to show up, whichever came first. Sergeant Kinney, a young fellow Jim had met up with who hailed from Virginia, lifted his glass and offered a toast, "To a boat home, leaky or not."

"To a boat home," the four men chorused, drinking deeply of the pale yellow-gold liquid.

"I'm not much of a drinker, but that beer has to be mostly water. Or is that my imagination," Jim asked the group.

Kinney answered, "I've had worse. I guess they are trying to make the beer last. Who knows how long we'll be here. They didn't expect to have to keep us entertained so long after we started heading for home."

"The latest news I got came from our captain. I thought he was going to chew me out again, and instead he told me to share the news that we are definitely heading to our Port of Embarkation on Thursday, November 22."

"We won't get our hopes up too high, Jim. We've had so dang many promises that I've stopped writing my family. They expected me by Thanksgiving. That's a few days off, but we won't have a chance to make it by then."

"I'm still writing, but just to my wife. I keep thinking that I'm writing my last letter from Europe — and then the next day comes and here I am still trying to find something interesting to put in another letter." Jim didn't know the other two men very well, and he looked at them for a moment as they sipped their diluted brews. Jim asked, "Where will you boys go when we get out of here?"

274

The man sitting on Jim's right answered quickly, some animation lighting up his face as he thought about his destination. "I'll be heading back to Oklahoma. My folks need me back almost as much as I need to be gone from this place."

The other man chimed in, "It looks like I'll be heading for the separation center back to Iowa. And it can't be too soon for me either. That center will get me within spitting distance of my folks' farmland."

The men nodded. Jim had just arranged that morning to change his separation center from Fort Meade in Maryland to Fort MacArthur, back in California. He figured it made more sense to get himself across the country and as close as possible to Irene. Fort MacArthur in California had launched him into this war from the induction center there before sending him on to the training at Camp Roberts. That would bring him full circle and much closer to his family. Plus, if they kept him there too long, Irene could come from Yuma and get there pretty easily.

Kinney looked at Jim's smile and commented, "Jim, you must like the music a whole lot. You just got a look on your face of pure enjoyment."

"Music? Oh, sure, that piano can talk. This is a nice place to wait around. But I'm smiling about what I will be doing once I get home. Sorry, I was eight thousand miles away for a minute there."

"No," Kinney replied, "I should apologize for bringing you back here." The four men shared rueful chuckles at this interchange.

One of the men from Jim's squad walked through the door and hollered out, "Truck's finally here. We're heading out."

"There's our signal, fellows. We leave tonight with the other NCOs to get instructions for our trip. Drink up, grab a sandwich, and let's get out of here. I can pass on the ping pong tonight."

The men left quickly to gather up their gear and meet back at the trucks earmarked for this next step in their journey. Jim, ever the faithful scribe, quickly sent a note to his wife telling her once again that it might be the last letter she got from Europe. He had decided he would probably stop reporting the promised dates of arrival, since in each letter he had to revise the last-promised date. At this point, he figured it just might be best to show up on her door step when he got there.

Chapter Thirty-nine

Marseille, France
November 26, 1945

My Dearest:

The long trek across Europe is finally finished, and I'm at last in Calais staging area in France. The trip down here took three days and nights in a boxcar, which they call 40 and 8's—meaning 40 men and 8 horses. We only rode 21 to a car, but it was still pretty rough. Good thing they left out the horses.

According to our C.O. we leave here December first or second, and will reach the states about the 12th. That will still put me home by Christmas. I sure hope you have gotten the packages I sent. I may be able to pick up something here if I can wangle a pass.

It is nice and sunny here, and we have cots, but it sure is cold at night. I have four blankets and a sleeping bag and damned near froze last night. Tonight, I'm going to wear an overcoat to bed.

We turned in our money for exchange today, and we fall out shortly for a 'flu shot. That is about all we have to do here except for numerous last-minute inspections. I may just get out of here alive after all. Hope I beat this letter home.

All my love,

Jim

The Mediterranean Sea is a quiet one, so perhaps I won't get seasick.

Determined to find the mail clerk and add his letter to the pile ready for transport, Jim stepped out of these most recent quarters in France with his overcoat and every other warm garment he could beg, borrow or liberate from the men huddled on cots in the tents. In spite of all the layers of clothing, the wind hit him like a two-ton block of ice from a packing shed.

He bowed his head into the wind, thinking that prayers wouldn't come amiss if he wanted to make it to the mail center and back without getting blown clear back to Germany.

A ten-minute walk in the gale-storm took twice the usual time, each step forward a hard-won victory over the force of the freezing cold and gusting wind. The sun was bright as hard laughter, offering little warmth.

He finally staggered into the mail clerk's station, a building of sorts, but not much more sturdy than the tents they had rigged up to house the waiting soldiers. The wind rattled at the walls, demanding entrance like a debt collector coming after the widow's overdue money.

"Hey, Jim, one of my best customers," the clerk greeted him as he stumbled through the door and stamped his boots at the entrance. "Matter of fact, you are my only customer today. Come on in and join me in a cup of lousy Joe. It's hot, but that's about all I can recommend for it."

"Thanks. I'll set a spell and warm up a bit before I head back out into that icy whirlwind. I appreciate it." Jim took the cup of coffee and sat on an overturned mail crate, hugging the cup close to let the steam warm his nose before he took a sip. He grimaced at the bitter brew, but made no comment.

"You'll be the first one I get to share the news with, Jim. Start spreading the word, though. This isn't rumor and it isn't good."

"What now?" Jim asked. He had a feeling he knew, and braced himself on the crate to hear it, expecting that mail delivery would not be possible because of the storm.

"Deployment is delayed. Again. This gale shows no sign of letting up, and the experts say it might get worse. The boats are all restricted to port for an undetermined time. You boys won't be going anywhere for a while. I'm sorry."

Jim said nothing for a moment, absorbing the thought of yet another delay, yet another excuse, and yet another false promise he had just given to his wife via his most recent letter. He took a huge gulp of the coffee, forgetting how horrible it tasted, and nearly spewed it out as the sour bitterness, matching his foul mood, flooded his mouth. Gasping as he swallowed, Jim choked out, "That coffee is nasty sludge, but your news is even worse. I'll tell you, things have sure been a mess for us — a month's stay in Ballendorf with the 12th Armored Division, a shift to 134th Ordinance, then to the 36th in Ulm, on to Blaubeuren for a month. Now we get stuck here in Calais. We've been given more excuses, from the New York Harbor strikes to the Britain recall of their ocean liners. Oh yeah, the ship we were first supposed to get on lost a propeller someplace. It never did show up. And now this crazy weather!"

"I can imagine that you are thoroughly disgusted with the Army," the clerk commiserated. "But we can't blame the Army for the weather. It almost feels like somebody up there is just tossing people around for laughs."

"It was the Army that sent us here to fight an impossible war, not expecting our outfit to survive. I guess it shouldn't surprise me none that they aren't prepared to manage transport for so many of us heading back home. They just didn't plan on needing to provide accommodations for all the G.I.s that are still around to make the return trip."

Jim's disappointment didn't stop him from trying to see the reasoning on the other side. And he already had started trying to think of a positive spin to this, revising his next letter to Irene in his mind. He went ahead and mailed the letter he carried, knowing that what he sent would have to be corrected in the next letter. At least he would have something to write about.

More than ever, he was tempted to start walking back by himself. But then an especially powerful gust of cold air rattled the clerk's rickety mail shack to remind him of the gale-force wind outside. He shivered as he hugged the hot, but lousy, coffee closer to his chest.

Chapter Forty

Marseille, France
December 7, 1945

My Dearest:

I remember the first letter I wrote when I found I was coming home—full of hope that I would be home by November 1 or the 5th at the latest. Even then I allowed a couple of weeks for delays, and here Christmas is fast approaching and I'm still on the wrong side of the water. My advice now is to look for me when you see me.

This place isn't too bad, but we are continually fighting in this tent. Stuck inside most of the time because of the bad storm, there's no way for the men to let off steam. And believe me, there's a lot of steam here, just not the kind to make us warm enough.

Have been learning to play bridge, believe it or not. The food is O.K. and we aren't too uncomfortable except on the mental side.

Tomorrow is your birthday, and in four days it will have been a year since I saw you last. Honey, you can't realize the years of time that one year has covered for me. I promise that I'll never leave you again, Army, war, or whatever else may come.

I know that the plans you have made for the past two months have been messed up, and I'm sorry now that I wrote that first letter that raised false hopes.

By some miracle, I could still make it for Christmas, but do not count on it, as there is bound to be more delay for us. I love you and hope that day we are together isn't too far off.

Forever, Jim

To top it all off, my shipping number is 13. Hope you aren't superstitious.

Irene sat on the rag rug floor of the new house in Yuma, the last of the boxes opened around her. The babies played quietly next to her, Jimmy finding his feet all over again, delighted with his discovery, and Ginger rocking back and forth, shaking a rattle and giggling at the noise. Grateful for these rare moments of relative calm, she fixed herself a cup of coffee and sat down again with Jim's last letter. It was dated December 7, 1945. That was over three weeks ago. The letter arrived on the sixteenth. She hadn't heard another word from him since.

She had tried not to worry, busy with the move from Winterhaven to the house her sister and brother-in-law had vacated when they moved to San Diego. She'd been thinking that maybe she and Jim could move from Yuma to settle there one day too. They really had nothing to take them back to Burbank.

San Diego stood south of Yuma and about a two-hour distance from her mother-in-law's front door. With Ray and Molly living there already, that would mean two of Jim's siblings living in cool California near the breezes by ocean waters. Moving there with Jim had a lot of appeal for Irene. But she would miss Pop Hendrickson terribly if they did go.

Impatient with her own dark thoughts, she walked across the room and plugged in the lights on the small tree she had decorated. Her hopes that her husband would be home for this special first Christmas for the twins dried out faster than the tree. But she smiled as both babies reacted with glee to the lights, laughing and staring, eyes wide with wonder.

Irene went back to Jim's letter, warming her hands on the mug, and read it over again. There were still no clues about how he was coping with his own disappointment. Knowing Jim, Irene figured he managed to put his best face on any situation, thinking to spare her cause for concern. But she knew her man — at least she knew the man she had married. She hoped he would be that same man when he came home to her.

The ringing phone startled her out of her quiet reverie, and she quickly grabbed a banana from the bowl on the table and handed each baby a piece. That should keep them quiet while she answered the line.

"Hello, this is Irene."

"Hi, dear, it's Pop."

"Well, hello, Pop. Happy day-before-Christmas," Irene responded. "Are you planning on playing Father Christmas tonight for these two little rascals I've got here?"

"That's why I called, Irene. I know I said we would come over for Christmas Eve supper with you and the kids. It is hard for you to take them out, and all. But Kittie says she is feeling a bit poorly. I was hoping you would be willing to come here and have dinner with us tonight. I'll pick you up so you won't have to worry about driving yourself and the two babies."

Irene thought for a minute. She should have expected this. Mom H seemed to find any excuse at all not to go out, and the only times Mom H had seen the babies were when Irene took them to visit her. Well, fine, she thought to herself. Let her do the cooking and cleaning up. She didn't want to deny Pop a chance to spend Christmas Eve with his grandchildren.

"I'm sorry she's not feeling well. Do you want me to bring anything for dinner? I'll be happy to do that. And thanks for offering to come and get us but I think I can catch a ride with Hazel and Mrs. Lawler. Are they invited too?"

"Yes, they are. I hadn't thought, but those two would no doubt love to carry you and the babies to us. Don't worry about food. Your mother-in-law will have a mountain of things to eat, for sure. Even when she is feeling off, she has the oven on."

"Ok, Pop! I'll call Hazel and set it up. See you about six tonight?"

"That's great, honey. Mary and Kay will probably have some of their young friends too. We'll make it a party and spoil the heck out of those babies of yours for their first Christmas."

Irene hung up the receiver, planning to look up Hazel's number. She looked at the babies who had as much banana on them as in them and went for a wash cloth instead. She felt glad of the need to keep busy and moving. An outing and party with the children would get her through one more day of anxious worry, wondering and waiting to hear if her husband had yet made it across the seas to the states.

Chapter Forty-one

Jim wasn't at all certain that his first telegram had reached Irene in Arizona. Stuck at Camp Patrick Henry in Virginia, he had broken down and spent some precious funds to send it, only to recall that he wasn't at all certain where his wife was living. Last he had heard, she was about to move, so he had sent the telegram, addressed to her, but in care of his parents at their home in Yuma.

ARRIVED SAFELY. EXPECT TO SEE YOU SOON. DON'T ATTEMPT TO CONTACT OR WRITE ME HERE. LOVE. JAMES.

He kicked himself again for his earlier request that she stop writing. He was back in the States but felt further away from her than ever. The United States Army had him jumping through hoops with their rules and regulations, and that was just to organize the paperwork and process him out. He should have been discharged months earlier.

He had saved back a precious few dollars from his dwindling funds, knowing they would have a long stretch to cover him until he got home. When word came that he would be sent to Fort Bliss in Texas for final processing, he decided to splurge on another telegram. He addressed this one to his wife in care of his parents too. He knew his folks' address and felt that he could trust Pop to give Irene both the information and some reassurance.

He didn't suppose that Irene had any chance of word from him. Surely none of his letters or V-mails could possibly have gotten to her while he traveled. Besides, the way the Army bounced him across the country from post to post, he hadn't gotten a firm arrival time until Fort Bliss, when he was finally released to travel to Los Angeles.

His one phone call once he reached the states had gone to his brother, Ray, who would be able to pick him up at the train station and carry him back home. Boy, those words sounded good in his mind, so he quietly voiced them, "Back home."

The clerk glanced up from his work, hearing Jim's quiet phrase and recognizing it as a sort of prayer. Jim saw the clerk's sympathetic smile and set back to the task at hand. He composed the second telegram with ever greater care, knowing his parents would see it before Irene did. He again addressed it to her in care of his parents, wondering where he would find his wife. For all he knew, she had finally moved in with his folks, though he rather doubted that.

He counted the words as he wrote because each added one made the damn thing cost even more. So he had to be brief:

AM IN ROUTE TO FT BLISS TEXAS. WILL BE HOME ABOUT JAN 5. LOVE. JAMES.

Crossing out the word *in* to put *en* would make it *enroute* instead. A preposition wasn't worth a dollar. Then he handed the text to the clerk to send. The clerk read it over, saw the misspelled word which should have counted as two, and let it go without a word.

"Merry Christmas, soldier. I hope you get there before New Year's Eve."

"Thanks, mister. I don't have any more business with the Army, so that should be possible to do. I can't tell you how good it feels to be in charge of myself again. Thanks, and Merry Christmas to you, too."

Jim glanced around at the decorations, still decking the halls of the Western Union Office. A worker had begun to take them down and box them for storage. He had missed Christmas entirely, holed up with Army red tape. They hadn't even allowed the men a chance to make phone calls on the holiday! He decided, not for the first time, that he was more than ready to walk the rest of the way home if he had to. If the Army transport didn't get him going right away, he would just put his hateful boots back on and hit the road on his own.

Those boots were a sore point, too. He didn't want to come home wearing them, but they hadn't let him pitch them over the side of the *Queen Mary* after all. He'd had to settle on doing things their way, including having to walk on United States soil with the German mud still clinging to his soles. Then, shuttled from post to post with no chance to buy replacements, he was stuck with the boots still.

He had learned to compromise in the Army, if nothing else. The Army still thought they owned him, but back in America, he felt like it was past time to take ownership and start making his own decisions. It was past time to take charge of his life again.

With a determined stride in spite of the boots, Jim thanked the telegraph clerk once more and left the office. His next steps would take him to the train station where he would finally be on his way to Los Angeles. That was one giant step closer to Irene.

Chapter Forty-two

Jim got off the train at Union Station in Los Angeles, feeling like a piece of chewed hard tack from one of his field kits. Then he remembered — no more field kits for him! He shook hands with the two soldiers who had shared the last part of the long trek with him on the train to the Los Angeles station. He wished them well and waved goodbye.

These two men had shared this last leg of the journey in enforced company with fellow soldiers. They still wore their uniforms, a condition of traveling for free, but he and the men agreed that this was the final vestige of connection with the military for each of them. He probably would never see these two men again, even though, of all the men he had fought with in Germany, these two probably lived closest to him geographically. Both boys were from the LA area, and they were in as much of a hurry to get home as he was.

Jim grabbed up his duffel bag and headed down the concourse from the trains, looking for his brother and consciously beginning the transition to civilian life once more. Searching for Ray in the large, echoing hall, he gave little notice to the beauty of the train depot. The last time here, he had gawped like a tourist, but this time his thoughts were too turbulent to enjoy the sights.

Another bit of irony struck him as he gazed around looking for Ray. He'd spent the last eighteen months searching for one brother, Bill, and now, here he was, almost home, and still looking for his brother. Only this time, the brother, Ray, would be the one to take him home to Irene. Bill was still far away from home, but safely back from his part in the war with his wife's family instead. Jim suspected it would be a good while yet before he would see his other brother, the liberated prisoner of war.

The slap on the back took him by surprise, as Ray yelled, "Jimmy" in his ear. He turned to look at Ray, and the two, not schooled in open displays of affection, shook hands with a tight grasp that neither would release. Ray spoke first.

"You son of a gun, you made it back in one piece. Thank you for that."

"You look good Ray. I was beginning to think I would have to walk across the desert from here, so I'm real glad to see you showed up. Where's Molly?"

At the question, Ray released Jim's hand clasp. "Long story, Jim. Let's get in the car and we can talk as we head out. I'm gassed up and we have water for the trip. We won't waste time. Mom is expecting us."

Jim didn't say anything as he finally took in the sights of the main hall of the Los Angeles train station. It sure was a beautiful place, with ceilings high enough to put another story or two in without raising the roof. The whole place hummed with the coming and going of hundreds of people, many were soldiers, and every person in the room had a story to tell.

He watched a man in uniform catch a toddler up into his arms and hold on to the tyke like a life preserver thrown from a boat in ocean waters. The man had tears streaming down his face as he looked over the child's shoulders at the elderly couple who had brought the baby. Jim wondered where the child's mother was, a jarringly missing piece in this happy jigsaw puzzle of homecoming.

Jim glanced at Ray and began to enjoy his own feelings of being back with family. Ray's comments about Molly were cryptic and Jim sensed trouble there. Ray's remark about

"Mom waiting for us" held a hint of warning for some ominous storm clouds that he didn't want to face. Already, he might soon be caught up in a power struggle that had little to do with Germans, prisoners of war, or world domination. He wondered if his mother's neurotic needs would present a fiercer challenge than these past few months of his Army duties. He wouldn't want to take bets one way or the other.

Jim maintained his quiet until he had tossed the duffle bag in the back of Ray's sedan, and they started out on the Los Angeles street toward the road that would take them through San Bernardino. That would get them going in the right direction to the desert trails southwards to Yuma.

"So how are Mom and Pop doing?"

"They are fine, though Pop still isn't fully recovered from the accident. He gets around ok though. Mom is healthier than she lets on, I think. That's part of why Molly isn't with me." Ray shook his head a bit and sighed. "My Molly... She didn't do too well with our mother when we were in Yuma. Our move to San Diego caused a ruckus, you know? I'm beginning to think Mom and Molly share some character traits in common. They are both stubborn and want their own way about things. And I'm not so sure that I am as good at handling that kind of thing as our Pop."

"I got that impression when I heard about Molly in your letters and from Irene. She seems like a great gal, though, Ray. And like Mom, she seems to have a good heart. Mom's problem is that she has just always enjoyed being taken care of."

"That's right, Jim. And Pop doesn't mind being the one to pamper her, that's for sure. But I'm caught in the middle trying to keep both women happy. Plus, Molly didn't like being expected to cater to Mom. She called her *Madame LaZonga*, and that's when she *wasn't* mad at her."

Jim laughed out loud at that, probably the first real laughter he had enjoyed for several days. There hadn't been too much to joke about during the difficult journey back across the country. But he wouldn't dwell on that. He decided to clear up his question to Ray directly.

"So why is Mom expecting us. What about Rene?"

Ray socked him in the arm, "Boy, nothing gets by you. It never did. You caught that, did you?"

Ray took a deep breath and gathered his thoughts. "Well here's the deal. Irene does not even know you are coming. Pop tells me that Mom kept your telegrams to herself, saying she wanted Irene to be surprised. She hadn't even shown those messages to Pop! We know, that really, she just figured how you have no idea where Irene is living right now.

"So that means she will have you all to herself for a while because we will have to go to the parents' house first to get Irene's address. But I promise — I will get you home to Irene within an hour of hitting Yuma. Dad won't let Mom keep you. He doesn't stand up to her too often, but he is perturbed with her about this little shenanigan."

Jim fumed. He loved his mother, but this had to stop. "You know, Ray, that's just not right. I should be going home to my wife and babies, not to my mother's house."

"I know, Jimmy. I'm sorry. Molly planned that we would take the twins, if Irene would let us babysit. That way you two could have had a nice reunion all on your own. When she found out what Mom had pulled with the telegrams, she refused to come down, so now, we don't have much choice. We need to do this Mom's way this time, and then I'll get you to Irene. She sure is a swell gal. And those babies are something else, I'll tell you."

"I get the lay of the land, Ray. I'll do this her way, but I'll be watching the clock tick until you take me to my wife. Better yet, I'll borrow Pop's car as soon as I get that address. That way you can hang around and visit with them after I leave to calm Mom down. Good lord. This takes almost as much strategy as fighting the Krauts!"

The miles of the desert began to stretch out in front of the two brothers, as they left the city behind and ventured out of populated areas and past San Bernardino into the empty wilds of sand and cactus. The humming of the tires cast a rhythm of calm, encouraging reflection.

Ray glanced in his rearview mirror at the last of the mountains, enjoying the contrast of the green hills and asphalt behind them with the open sky and sand ahead. Then he looked at Jim gravely. His younger brother had fallen into a sorrowful quietness.

"How hard a time did you have over there? I mean, I know I got soft duty stateside. So many guys who have come back just haven't been whole. How are you? Really…"

Jim roused himself from his darker thoughts. "It was a rough deal, all right, Ray. Rougher than I care to dwell on, to tell the truth. My plan is to leave all of it behind, like this ugly pair of boots I'm ready to throw out into the desert."

"Do it, Jim. Toss the damned things out and let the scorpions play house in them. That should give Mom something to think about when you show up barefoot."

So Jim, laughing out loud, finally took off the hated boots, looked them over, and noted that they still had mud caked in the soles, deep in the tracks that ran from heel to toe.

"I just hope the parents still have some of my clothes at the house. I know Irene does, wherever she lives. But I would hate to show up at her house barefoot."

"No need to worry. If they don't have a pair to fit you, you can use mine. We wear about the same size as I recall. Unless you changed shoe sizes in Germany."

With that, Jim took off both boots. "Heck on fire, Ray. I barely ever these boots off, let along change shoe sizes."

Ray slowed the car down, and, with great ceremony, Jim pitched out the hated boots into the stretch of sand alongside the road. He watched one, and then the next, bounce at the landing and kick up a small cloud of dust from the desert as it hit. Each made its own miniature mushroom-cloud-like formations, as though from a bomb blast in the salt-textured earth among cactus plants that pointed prickly fingers skyward.

"That's that," he said as Ray sped up again. "Good thing I have on extra socks."

Ray glanced down at Jim's feet and watched Jim wiggle his toes. He laughed out loud at what appeared to be four — maybe five — pairs of socks bunched on his brother's bootless feet. "Tell me that isn't every pair of socks you own, Jim."

"That's right, Ray. And every pair is mine, not the Army's. I've had warm feet since I hit the States, and I don't ever want to get them frozen again."

The trip across the desert took nearly four more hours, but the two brothers made the miles pass quickly, catching up with each others' lives and recalling favorite people and events from the past, before the war took robbed them of their innocent youth.

When they crested the lonely hill overlooking the stretch of white sand dunes, Jim felt his heart swell. This hill heralded homecoming and he had dreamed about it in foxholes he now wanted to forget completely.

Within fifteen minutes from the rest stop by Gordon's Well, and on through the desert past the California dunes of Thermal, they finally drove through the tiny town of Winterhaven, a mile from the Colorado River crossing into Arizona.

Pop's service station bustled with business, but they didn't take time to stop. Instead, they continued out of the one-block-long town and headed across the narrow bridge that crossed the Colorado River to enter Arizona.

Ray soon pulled up at 665 Second Avenue in Yuma. The house, remodeled as a duplex, had sheltered his parents and their six children for most of the years of Jim's childhood. It now offered Jim a friendly welcome with a spruced-up white brick face, fresh from the recent renovations.

Pop met them at the top of the steps, on a wide porch that shaded two separate entry halls. A cane in his right hand supported his spare frame. His frail appearance gave Jim a tug of sad surprise. He called a greeting, and Pop waved, giving Jim a chance to look him over carefully before climbing up to join him on the broad porch at the top of the stone steps. His father had aged, lost weight, and he looked gray and thin. He hugged his father close, slapping him lightly on the back.

"Welcome home, Son. God bless you and keep you, it's good to see you here."

"Thanks, Dad. It's good to be back, but I'm not home yet, you know that."

"Yes, I do, son. You take a few minutes with your Ma and eat a quick bite with her. I figure you might want to take my car and go see a pretty little gal over at the Eighth Avenue property. You remember the house I'm talking about?"

"We always did think alike, Dad. Thanks. I do know the house. It's the one that you built catawampus and sideways, so you don't enter from the street. How is my Irene?"

"She is a wonder, son. I have never known such a strong little lady in my whole life. She works miracles with those two babies. I know you can't wait to see her..."

A querulous voice called faintly from inside. "Jimmy? You out there, Jimmy?"

Jim picked up his duffle, and Ray joined them on the steps, ready to enter into the fray together. "You know, before today is over I am going to make it clear to Mom that I don't go by Jimmy any more. It's Jim ... and Irene."

Both men nodded with understanding grins at Jim's gumption. They might not bet against Kittie Hendrickson, but it was obvious that Jim was no longer a boy.

Jim gave a nod, understanding their unspoken doubt and support at the same time. He glanced at his watch before he spoke again. "Ray, look at your watch. Mine says 11:00 a.m.?"

"That's what mine says, Jim," Ray responded back firmly.

"Well, at noon, I am taking a drive. You may have to create a diversion so that I can, but that's definite. Are we clear, men?"

Jim's father and brother snapped a quick salute and said, "Yes sir, Jim sir," and they watched him walk toward the front door.

Pop leaned over to Ray and whispered quietly, "Where in Sam Hill are his shoes? I didn't want to ask, but his mother is certain to notice."

Ray didn't answer his father, but instead started laughing hard enough to make Jim turn around.

"Jim," he said, "it seems we forgot that you might have some explaining to do about why you came home in your sock feet. Have you got a good story to tell?"

And with that, Jim just grinned. "I'll think of something before Mom starts in on me about it."

The three men joined in more laughter, arms around each others' shoulders, sharing the joy of welcoming back brother, son and soldier. Together, the three men headed through the front doors and on through the hallway to the living room where Jim's mother waited for them to attend her.

Chapter Forty-three

Irene took down the last of the ornaments from the tree, packing them neatly away to use next year. Her favorite ones tinkled merrily as she placed them in cotton packing, tiny solid silver bells, a shining Christmas gift from Pop. When he gave them to her, he had told her that she should always hang them on the branches lowest enough for her smallest child to reach. They would signal a pleasant alarm if a young one got too brave about playing with the decorations or sneaking a peek at wrapped packages. She would treasure them, as she treasured Pop Hendrickson.

She wished the tree would have lasted until Jim got home. The dry desert heat had sucked out every drop of moisture, leaving bone-dry needles that had begun to drop in noiseless flight to sprinkle their landing path all over her clean floor. She hadn't lit the lights on the tree for three days for fear of sparking a fire from the dry pine.

Wrapping the small, browning evergreen into sheets of newsprint for disposal, she glanced to make sure both babies were still safely in their two cribs. She blessed Mom, Pop and Mrs. Lawler who had come up with a second bed. She suspected that while Mrs. Lawler had no doubt found the crib, her in-laws had probably paid for it. They would think it unseemly to have Jim come home and find his son sleeping in a laundry basket.

She finished her task, putting away the boxes and sweeping up the last of the Christmas residue. Her new house was in order again. The twins had eaten their lunch already, and the babies jabbered contentedly, their noise incomprehensible to anyone but each other.

The wall clock that she and Jim had purchased for their first apartment in Burbank chimed the noon hour, a signal that her children would soon talk themselves into sleep for their afternoon nap. She figured she would fix a sandwich or something for her own lunch soon.

Walking quietly out of the living room with a small smile and a sense of accomplishment, she looked at her newly organized kitchen, appreciating how much easier this home made life for her. She shuddered to recall the first residence she had occupied in Yuma, over the garage in back of Mom and Pop's place. Counting her blessings, she gave a soft prayer of thanks, with a reminder to the Lord to please bring her Jim home safe. She hoped it would be soon.

Putting away her worry about him, she decided to trust in the Lord to get him here, one way or another. Still, it had been too long since she had heard from him. But she refused to let it get her down. She had to trust Jim as much as the Lord — and she felt like she had every right to count on both.

She could tell by the quieting sounds in the bedroom that the twins were settling in for a good, long nap. She could always find more chores to do, but she decided to treat herself instead. Pouring out a cup of leftover coffee from the pot, she headed back to the living room toward the shelves. She started to choose a book, and instead picked up the last letter Jim had sent her. That gave her one more quick chore to finish before she would let herself relax. She put down her hot coffee to cool and reached up to the top shelf.

The sturdy brown box held each letter Jim had sent since the very first one he had mailed from his first days as a soldier. In orderly rank and file, each stacked by date in its envelope, still stamped or marked "FREE" by the U.S. Postal Service, the letters fit perfectly into the space.

Giving the most recent precious missive a quick kiss as a seal, she filed it carefully in its place at the very back of the box. It fit snuggly, so much so that it made Irene hope that there would be no more letters to add. She would rather have him home than stuck somewhere writing more letters. She would also hate to have to start another box. This one held over a thousand pages Jim had sent to her from across the miles. "Heavens, that should be enough," Irene said to herself.

At last, she picked up her book and her still-warm cup. Then, Irene crossed over to the sofa by the window that faced out onto the front street. Plumping up the pillows on the couch, she pulled the curtains aside to let in just a bit more light for reading. A gray sedan like Pop's had just pulled up to the curb, and a soldier got out. He seemed to be looking at the house.

"That's odd," she said out loud, thinking his actions as strange — this soldier must be lost. She noticed another oddity. While in Army uniform, this man had civilian shoes on. He walked as though the shoes pinched his feet a little as he stepped forward gingerly but with purpose along the path towards the side driveway from the street.

She expected him to head towards the neighbor's house; most folks did that until they located the "front" door that was on the south side of their oddly-placed home. But instead, he disappeared from view. Curious, she leaned further out into the window, trying to figure out the soldier's destination.

She could see out pretty well from the living room that had no door to the street, through the bay windows facing west onto the road. That was the unique thing about Pop's design of this home. One would expect the front door to be on the street side, next to the sofa where she stood looking out the front window. Instead, the door to the main entrance faced south, onto a driveway between the neighboring homes.

Out of view from her vantage point, Irene thought this poor soldier must be pretty sharp to figure it out so fast if he was headed to her door. Most folks walked around gawking and scratching their heads a bit before they found the entrance on the side of the house. She was thinking that maybe he was a friend of Virginia and Eb, her in-laws who had lived here before she and the babies moved in. This soldier probably expected to find them still in residence.

And then Irene heard a firm knocking on her locked door at the side of the house. She glanced quickly at her now-sleeping twins and hurried to unlock the door and open before the noise could wake them.

When she saw the face of the soldier, her eyes opened even wider than the door — and she opened her arms just as wide to bring Jim home at last.

Epilogue

After the war, Jim and Irene made a life for themselves, just as so many other young couples did in those bygone days of the 1940's. They counted themselves among the fortunate number of those who came through the Second World War in one piece. While Dad may have soured on the Army experience in general, he never waivered in showing respect and honor for those who served.

Jim and Irene stayed in Yuma and Jim took over Pop Hendrickson's service station in Winterhaven, CA. Pop Hendrickson never did fully regain his health, so his son also worked the land grant, planting orange orchards and watching them thrive.

This was merely a partial fulfillment of his dream of becoming a farmer, but it didn't last long. In 1958 when Pop Hendrickson died, that land was sold and divided among all Jim's brothers and sisters equally. My father always said that he would like to have owned his own farm, but it just wasn't in the cards dealt to his hand.

The year Pop passed away from heart failure, Jim was appointed to fill out Pop's term as Justice of the Peace in Winterhaven. He kept the station going too. Working seven days a week, he still managed to keep an eye on his mother and his family. Irene stayed home with the twins, Virginia and Jimmy. Four years after Dad came home from war, I was born, followed by my youngest brother, Michael, six years later in 1955.

Jim and Irene worked hard and, always a great team, they made good on Jim's goal to send all four of us to college. In 1972, Jim was appointed Yuma County Assessor to finish up the elected official, Otis Ship's term. He retired from the service station, and helped his mother sell it to capable management.

He and my mother did some traveling as part of their association with Eastern Star. Jim became more active as a 32nd Degree Mason and he and Irene were installed as Worthy Matron and Patron of the Yuma Eastern Star Organization.

He also was able to attend church on Sundays with my mother, something he hadn't done for many years. I was off to college during this time and didn't see it, but my younger brother tells me that sometimes our parents held hands as they sat in the pew of the First Christian Church.

As Jim prepared to run for a full term in the elected office as County Assessor, he fell ill and had to withdraw from a declaration of candidacy. Frequent trips to Phoenix for medical treatment made life hard for my mother and father. Visits to my small family in Avondale were the one earnest blessing we could enjoy whole-heartedly those days as Dad and his three-year-old grandson grew close.

But he continued to grow more frail and fragile, smiling when anyone looked his way, but fading as we watched. Doctors could not give an exact diagnosis of what ailed him, but they kept running tests and procedures that weakened him even more. Dad succumbed to what was described as "a unique cancer of the blood" in 1974. He was only 52 when he passed away.

Irene's 96th birthday falls on December 8, 2018. She is a resident on the Memory Care floor at Oakmont, Chino Hills, just five minutes from our home in Southern California. I visit her every day and take her coffee to start her morning on a warm note. We still find much to "cuss and discuss" about.

While her memory is not always reliable, she maintains a gracious quality, enjoying good conversation and frequent visitors. If someone mentions her Jim, she still glows warmly with a soft twinkle in her eye.

AUTHOR'S NOTE

Letters used in this novel remain unchanged. In order to tell the story, some letters are excerpted or combined for the sake of brevity or to avoid repetition. The narrative backstory for the letters is partially fictional, based on author research and recollection of stories told by family members. While some of it may be fiction, it is, to the best of my ability, true. Any factual errors are probably mine. The entire collection of letters written by Private James William Hendrickson, Jr, along with photographs from the period can be found at: **hewrotehereveryday.com**. A Facebook page offers daily posts that dovetail with the dates of Dad's letters. These can be found on **Facebook/HeWroteHerEveryDay**. The entire collection of Dad's letters can now be found in New Orleans, LA, USA at the National WWII museum. Kim Guise, curator of the museum, is working on a display of all the letters and souvenirs donated by the Hendrickson family. Dad's letters are the largest compendium of letters written by a single soldier. They stand as primary witness to world events from a voice of the common man who became a soldier and walked through snow in Germany fighting a "war to end all wars" while he searched for his brother.

I owe a debt of gratitude to the staff of Sapere Books for having faith in my book. Amy Durant and Caoimhe O'Brien worked diligently on organization and flow of my earlier version of the book. Their patience and kindness made this project a pleasure.

I am always happy to hear from people who read Dad's story, the book, and/or the letters. Feel free to contact me via my email, xlindy@aol.com.

Thank you for reading Jim and Irene's story...

Sapere Books is an exciting new publisher of brilliant fiction and popular history.

To find out more about our latest releases and our monthly bargain books visit our website: **saperebooks.com**

55182109R00182

Made in the USA
Middletown, DE
15 July 2019